Praise fo

The House in B

Part memoir, part travelogue *The House in Bausasran* is an evocative reflection on how cross-cultural engagement has shaped a life. This richly detailed account presents the fascinating story of a young Australian's initial engagement with the hippie trail, based around the Sumarah spiritual movement in the Javanese court city of Solo where international travellers gathered in the 1970s and 80s to study meditation. The juxtaposition of this youthful experience with the account of returning to live in Java two decades later is framed by the beginning and end of a marriage, an enduring process of self-awareness and realisation about love, liberty and loneliness. With a sharp memory for detail, Wynne Taylor has recreated a vivid sense of the outsiders' fascination with Javanese culture, and the excitement tinged with doubt that comes with being in another culture.

—Siobhan Campbell

Through a story of self-transformation, Wynne Taylor weaves together the colourful strands of life with a backdrop of Indonesian culture and history, skilfully blending a rich sense of place with intricate detail. Masterful storytelling!

—Ella Ruth

As a heart can be broken into a thousand scattered pieces, Teresa Wynne Taylor has brilliantly told the story of how these fragments can be so delicately pieced together again into a mosaic of love, acceptance, courage and hope. Poignant, at times humorous, I found myself so moved as I was brought along on this tender and beautiful journey, falling in love with Lara's Indonesian family and community.

—Anna Toso

with love
Teresa
April
2023

The House in Bausasran

TERESA WYNNE TAYLOR

ISBN 978-1-922784-49-0 (paperback)
ISBN 978-1-922784-50-6 (ebook)

Artwork by Circle Brophy
Printed and bound in Australia by Clark & Mackay

A catalogue record for this book is available from the National Library of Australia

A portion of the sales of this book goes to support
Bina Sewi Orphanage, Bantul, Yogyakarta, Indonesia.
(See www.teresawynnetaylor.com for more information)

For Nikki & Raya

Semuanya berawal dari mimpi

Everything begins with a dream

Said a sheet of snow-white paper,
"Pure was I created, and pure will I remain forever.
I would rather be burnt and turn to white ashes than suffer darkness to
touch me or the unclean to come near me."
The ink bottle heard what the paper was saying,
and it laughed in its dark heart;
but it never dared to approach her.
And the multicoloured pencils heard her also,
and they never came near her.
And the snow-white sheet of paper did remain pure and chaste forever
- pure and chaste - and empty.

--oOo--

Kahlil Gibran

Prologue

Not enough has been said about Harto—about his humility for one thing and its importance to him, and even after all that happened, his strength and honour. But in relating his story I must reveal a part of my own, of an enduring love and friendship woven together from the warp and weft of two different cultures. Sometimes life can stand up and surprise you when you are at your lowest ebb and a tide of grief has swept you out and abandoned you at sea. When it seems all hope of happiness is lost, it can drag you in and wash you up on a less familiar but friendly shore.

Part One

1

Bausasran, Yogyakarta, Java
July 2008
Dry Season

Across the dusty, potholed lane stands an Old Dutch Colonial house nestled under a cluster of shady coconut palms in languid style. Its wooden walls are slightly sagging; its former glory long gone, weather-beaten now, from years under Indonesia's tropical sun. A signpost in the front proclaims it as the *Partai Peduli Rakyat Nasional*: The Party that Cares for the Nation's People. A decade of democratic reforms has seen political parties flourish here. They seem to bloom overnight like bright coloured flowers in an unruly garden and sometimes topple over just as quickly.

I like to imagine this ageing house was lifted one night from its foundations and dipped in a giant vat of red paint, to be returned at daybreak by the party faithful, transformed into its Yogyakarta headquarters. Not a crevice has been spared from the pot. Gutters, downpipes, doors and trim all coated in the same vibrant shade. The colour red is popular here. Even the rusty picket fence is painted red.

Red and white are the colours of the Indonesian flag. Colours that represent the brave and bloody battle fought for independence after World War II. One legend tells how the tricolour flag of the ruling Dutch was brought down in a frenzy of patriotism, its royal blue stripe ripped off in the mayhem and the two remaining colours paraded through the streets of Surabaya. The red, the crowds had shouted, was for victory and the blood that was spilled—the white for peace. Indonesians claimed these colours as their own and at the same time claimed their country back. This is a proud nation.

A giant mango tree graces the front verge, stretching its gnarled branches skyward. For part of the year, it rains mangoes. Barefoot children clamber up its sturdy boughs and hook the more stubborn ones that refuse to fall. This is their world and it seems like a good omen.

Sometimes in the late afternoon when dusk begins to fall, a cacophony of playful cries and laughter—of bicycle skids and children's chatter—will lure me from my desk to the front windows where, gazing out through a rustle of green foliage, my eyes can't help but glimpse those transformed remnants of a faded colonial past.

These images though familiar now still cause me to wonder at my own fate, and the unexpected twist of it that found me living here, surrounded by the scent of spices and the earthy smell of tropical downpours, not far from the foot of a live volcano. I wonder at how fate managed to reel in another chance from the depths of opportunity and lead me to this very different life. A life enticed by the promise of possibility, freedom, new discoveries and my own independence within the heart of a Javanese family, in another Old Dutch Colonial house—the pale green one that looks out over the bold red one.

2

I drift out of sleep in the mornings here to the smoke and crackle of smouldering garden refuse, mixed with yesterday's kitchen scraps and the swishing sound of Aji sweeping leaves from the paths around the house; paths of sandy black volcanic soil, stamped as hard as stone from human tread and time. A rooster struts about a nearby yard proclaiming his hen harem as his alone. Scooters, ferrying children to a nearby school, rev their clackety engines. Food peddlers push past the front windows with rickety carts luring a neighbourhood into the street with their steaming selections of *bubur*. Each peddler has a different call. The locals recognise them all. They know which tap-tap-tap of spoon on bowl means sweet mung bean porridge, and they know the ting-ting-ting that signals savoury rice. They know the musical jingle of the sweet bread seller.

Whenever I linger in bed listening to the bustle of sounds that bring this royal city to life, I know that Aji will be hungry and waiting for the hollow sound of a bamboo stick beating a slow rhythm on a dented saucepan lid. It's the sound of the old man selling *bubur ayam:* rice porridge drowned in spicy chicken broth—his favourite.

Aji has worked here for the past few months as my *pembantu.* Sometimes I hear the word translated into English as servant and shrink at its demeaning ring. Perhaps I'm overly protective, and sometimes too sensitive, and I'm told I worry too much for my own good. After all, Aji does not speak English and so—should he happen to overhear the word in an English conversation—would not be offended. Aji is fine, and for now all is well. In any case pembantu comes from the root word *bantu* which means 'to help' and we can all use a bit of that sometimes.

The umbrella language of Indonesian seems to me infused with kindness, and a politeness, which aims to instil a mutual respect and bind a sprawling country of haves and have-nots; so that where circumstance has been less benevolent a sense of pride can be maintained. Though there will always be some who look down upon domestic helpers I hope never to be counted amongst them. We can all be cock of the roost one day and feather duster the next. This I have learned only too well.

So Aji helps with the daily chores and maintenance. His presence helps to make this house a home, though it was his skill in carpentry that first brought him here to the tumbledown charm of the house in Bausasran.

He came soon after Harto persuaded him with the offer of a job. They already knew each other well and I knew them both—the older and the younger equally resourceful and in Harto's case more than dependable. They had repaired a house and rescued a garden for me once before, in the city of Sidoarjo, East Java. Now Harto and I needed help with this one in Yogyakarta, five hours to the west.

Harto had stumbled across the house as if it was meant to be. I imagine its green gables must have beckoned against the pale blue sky like a bridge. A bridge in the form of a house that could help him to balance two worlds—the one he knew well and the Western one that blew in unexpectedly with me.

He was visiting his elderly mother, Ibu Daliyah, at the time. She wasn't well and I knew that above all else he needed to be with her. She, who was the anchor of his world, had recently taken a fall in the family kampung. Harto said she had slipped on a lichen-covered path in the rain as she hurried back from the communal bathrooms to her tiny house at dusk.

I had insisted he return home from the house in Sidoarjo as soon as we heard the news, and that I would be fine, and to take his time until she was well; or at least until Galuh, his sister returned home from the beach at Cilacap. "Galuh, should have been taking better care of their frail mother," he said. He never trusted Galuh with anything and this was more proof to add to the list of her sibling misdemeanours.

"Ibu has hit her head badly and her body is very bruised," he said, sounding unsettled when he telephoned later. "But I have been lucky too," he added, his deep voice tumbling more positive news down the line. "I have found a house for you not far from the kampung. I think you will like it very much. The ceilings are the high ones you prefer and the rooms are spacious. You will not have to worry about feeling confined," he assured, knowing that an airy feel would be at the forefront of my mind.

"Unfortunately, I cannot leave Ibu until Galuh comes back, but I think you should come as soon as possible to see if you like it, and to meet the landlord, Pak Yuda. I will try to organize for Pak Sungkar to drive you here tomorrow. He will be happy to repay us for all the support we gave to his family last year."

Dear Pak Sungkar, I thought. He had recently lost his wife to kidney failure after months of treatment; and at such a young age. She wasn't yet forty. It seems life is not easy for any of us. I thanked Harto for his kindness and told him how sorry I was to hear about his mother's poor condition. "Everything is fine here," I assured him. "Please stay with her for as long as you need."

In an earnest mix of English and Indonesian he replied, "I will accompany you back on the Argo Wilis," and added quietly, "We can relax and enjoy the train ride from Yogyakarta to Surabaya together.

3

I was in Sidoarjo, on the far outskirts of Surabaya, that evening, contemplating the task of packing up a household of possessions, amongst them a few basic pieces of furniture collected over the previous year. The list included a queen-size spring bed, a study desk, some makeshift bookshelves, a small dark wood dining table with two matching chairs, along with a more luxurious Persian floor rug. I had purchased this artisan piece a few weeks before from the famous Middle Eastern market store in Surabaya, indulging an opportunity I feared might not arise again.

The carpet, created from soft woollen yarns, was dyed in the organic colours of plant-green and madder-red, woven into a pattern of oriental flowers and leaves, adding a touch of style that soothed my aesthetic senses. Sadly though, not imbued with the fabled flying power of Aladdin's and thus unable to uplift all my belongings to Yogyakarta.

Harto loved the stories I told him of Aladdin—about his magic lamp and flying carpet—though he knew of them and knew many other stories of magic too, raised as he had been on the mystical island of Java. But as far as moving the furniture he had conceded, hoisting himself onto an elbow as he ran his fingers over its soft pile, he would need to organise a small truck.

But we both agreed the carpet had other special powers. They lay in the blissful hours we spent wrapped in each other's arms on it, and in the firm footing it provided on the slippery white tiles of the living room floor. And for me there was a certain feel that flew in the front door with its arrival. The familiarity of a life I had left behind.

On the night that Harto called from Yogyakarta I was relaxing on the soft comfort of the carpet hugging my knees to my chest as we chatted on our small Nokia phones. The contents of the kitchen cupboards had been packed into plastic tubs, books and teaching materials from the study stacked into cardboard boxes, and an assortment of clothes were scattered haphazardly around me.

The clothes were being sorted into piles—those to be kept and those to be given away. I always had far too many. Buying new clothes had become a habit after years spent working in the world of fashion. Out with the old season and in with the new. That's how the industry kept its customers coming back.

Harto would eventually change that mindset. He would teach me to see the beauty and value of faded things. But it certainly took some time because he didn't teach me with words, but in the way he lived. And in the way we lived together.

"I will bring some clothes for Galuh," I said as we talked on our Nokias, and suggested a pair of cargo pants. They had been favourites for a while and fitted my figure well, but the black dye had faded and I knew she had high hopes I would pass them on to her. She had learned it would only be a matter of time before I replaced them with something new.

"Jangan buang bajunya ya, Juragan," she would say with a wink whenever she caught sight of me in the kampung. "Don't throw away your clothes, ya Boss. Second or third hand is still good for me."

Galuh was the first to call me Juragan, the Javanese word for boss. Later, the family would follow. They would take it upon themselves to elevate my position, against all my protestations.

Harto's older brother, Elang, would come by the house in Bausasran to explain one day. He would sit with me cross-legged on the same Persian floor rug, carefully polishing the lenses of his metal-framed glasses. He would rub the sadness of a mother's funeral and the long journey by ferry and rail to attend it from his tired eyes, and stroke the hairs of his moustache thoughtfully into place. Then he would politely offer a glass of jasmine tea from a tray that Harto, catching my eye with a mischievous grin, would place on the carpet before leaving his elder sibling to gently explain the hierarchical system of Javanese culture.

Elang would insist with a fatherly concern that it would be less confusing for the family if I could agree to oversee the running of the household, so that each could happily go about their business. He would gently suggest that I didn't need to give a helping hand, especially to Aji who took such pride in his work. He would say that he feared Aji was losing confidence. That Aji saw my help, here and there, as a sign of dissatisfaction.

A pearl-buttoned blouse, hand-washed and hung on the line in the garden before his very eyes, stabbed at his heart. Aji, whose job it was to do the laundry. Aji, who was more fastidious than most could ever hope to be—crushed by my ignorance! I couldn't bear it. And right there, awakened out of my egalitarian world, I accepted the position, though rather uncomfortably, because I had been raised to pick up after myself.

But that was also the moment when the family took me wholeheartedly into their fold. Found a place for me they felt was fitting, so that each one knew how to stand in theirs. Not least of all Harto's wife Saraswati. There would be no need for any further explanation to her, or to anyone else regarding the nights that Harto spent with me. And that she, who had accepted this fate without complaint, would be able to keep face and keep her respected place.

After that jasmine tea infused meeting, it seemed the house along with its occupants breathed a long, slow sigh of relief and the freshly painted walls themselves relaxed, enough to catch the sunbeams pouring in through the front windowpanes.

However, all this was still in store. Waiting in the wings of a future I could never have imagined would be mine. I hadn't yet met Elang or his family, or Harto's older sisters, Ajeng and Santi, and their husbands, and all the children. Or Heru, his reclusive brother—of smaller build and lesser height—blind in one eye. All of this was still to come. When they all came together for their mother's funeral.

That night in Sidoarjo as I sorted through clothes and chatted with Harto, as if home was his deep voice on the other end of the line, I could never have imagined all the things that lay in wait.

The joy-filled moments and the mini-disasters, the house floods; the nuptial flight of the termites that filled the rooms of the house in Bausasran every November; the arrival of the new teak furniture and the giant clay pots; the batik curtains that Saraswati would make so caringly; the teachers at the English school and the friendships that lasted; all the learning and the lessons and the students' laughter; the dengue fever and all the love showered upon me; the volcanic eruption that saw the entire city—its temples and its palace covered with ash—its mountain dwellers made homeless. The tragic loss of Saraswati that unravelled us all, and through it all the richness in the lives that I witnessed, despite their having so little in the way of material possessions, their unquestioning acceptance of me. I had been blessed.

What a pity I wasted the first few years of it feeling so damaged. Devastated by what I had lost. Looking behind me for far too long at a door that had been firmly closed. If only we could be more like machines. Or at least have a setting to erase certain memories. Or remember to live in gratitude for what we have on a daily basis.

"The cargo pants will suit Galuh's athletic body and her tomboy style, Harto," I continued, hoping to persuade his gentler side.

"Be careful. Don't spoil Galuh, and don't give money," he warned. "Galuh is like a greedy cat, and later you will regret your kindness."

Harto was always full of warnings about Galuh and often she would push him too far and prove him right. But she was also a single mother of three daughters and that's what I saw. And I saw that her life was a daily struggle. She had managed to marry off her eldest, she told me proudly one day, to a man of means. But the two younger ones still needed to be clothed and fed.

I hadn't met Galuh's eldest daughter Leila then either, but I'll never forget the day I did. And the day I saw all the beauty pageant trophies she had won lined up on a tall cupboard in the front room of Galuh's home in the kampung.

We hadn't been at Bausasran long when Leila appeared one morning under the back garden *pendopo*. She had come to look for Galuh. I was padding barefoot out through the kitchen with a pile of books for Aji to cover when I caught sight of her. She and Aji were engaged in thoughtful conversation. I remember stopping mid-step to catch my breath, instantly regretting the dowdy housedress I was wearing, but it was too late to change. She had caught sight of me too through the window.

Her complexion was luminous. Her round face framed in a cropped pixie haircut, which in itself was unusual for a woman in Java, but suited her perfectly. If only I could describe her beauty as artfully as Arundhati Roy, or sing the praises of it in a crescendo as celestial as a boys' choir. But the best I can do is to say she had the kind of eyes that shine and flawless glowing skin, and that her equivalent in the West would have to be the young Grace Kelly herself. How could Harto, I wondered, have never mentioned her before.

"I am not interested in Leila," he said dismissively, when I asked about her later. "Her husband ignored my mother at their wedding," he added with a glower. "His behaviour can never be forgiven. I don't care about his wealth or position. He has no manners. And Galuh, she just cares about his money," he muttered, putting a stop to any more talk of it with a set jaw. That was Harto with his lion's pride.

Still, I threw the cargo pants into a pile of things destined for Galuh and some silver bangles for the girls. By then I knew that gold and silver jewellery in Java could always be traded or sold by weight, back to the *toko emas* gold stores or the *perak* silver stores from where it was bought. I had learned from Saraswati that the 22-carat gold jewellery a woman wore was akin to a savings account.

Among the array of clothing on the carpet that night in Sidoarjo three neatly folded stacks might have caught your eye. One of blue denim jeans in various shades, another of linen trousers in two basic colours; black and beige, and a collection of white shirts in various cottons, linens, and voiles. Alongside these was a collection of silk batik scarves in black and white patterns or the occasional burst of colour.

I had spent years in the fashion industry in Australia before turning my career to teaching English in Java, and had pared my wardrobe down to these few things. A simple look that I chose because life was complicated enough. The fact that covered arms were a must for Muslim women in Sidoarjo made the choice of sleeve length easier. Not that the rule was ever forced upon me, it was just what I noticed and was happy to follow, as I myself prefer an understated look when it comes to fashion.

All right, I admit to a Dior style skirt or two and a belted calf-length dress in a midnight-black French linen, thrown together on my trusty Elna Lotus sewing machine a week before I flew out of

Brisbane. And I suppose I did have an overabundance of white shirts. But each one had a different feature, either in the stitching or the shape of a pocket, the width of a cuff or the point of a collar, or in the texture of the fabric. These details appealed to my patternmaker's eye. And besides, there are many shades of white.

4

As I continued to cull the piles of clothing, I came across a white blouse I had bought two years before in Bali, and since then had worn only once. It was made from hand-embroidered Uluwatu lace. The kebaya style bodice fanned out from a fitted waist to the hip, matching the fan-shaped sleeves that fell softly over the wrists.

I held it up remembering the day I bought it with my husband, Angus. I had flown from Brisbane, especially to see him after three months of being apart. He flew in from Jakarta for a few days—promising to leave his briefcase and executive status behind—but the loving reception I had so longed for was absent. He was as cold and distant as Arctic ice, and sporting a new style of confidence that flirted with every young female in sight but failed to see me.

I spent a week wandering around the beaches of Sanur, aimlessly browsing through curb-side clothing stores in the main street, feeling as empty as a shell. Occasionally I would stop to eat at a café alone until, on the last day, I asked him to take a taxi with me to Uluwatu. I wanted to see how its famous lace was made.

He was working on his laptop at an Internet café near the beach when I found him, twinkling his blue-grey eyes and bantering with the female staff as if he was already a regular patron. He stretched his fine-freckled white arms over his head in a yawn when I asked, and said he supposed that he could. He slid the laptop into a carry case and slung it over his shoulder, flicking the sweat from his brow onto the sand as he pulled his wallet from the back pocket of his long chino shorts and signalled for the bill.

He was twenty kilos larger than the slim young man I had married and the extra weight was all around his middle, but he wore it with his head held high and without apology. I dared not reach for his hand fearing rejection. He did not offer his. How I missed his touch and how paralysed I felt in my longing for it because, despite his overindulgent decline into middle age and his tendency to arrogance, he was still my husband. The man I had married in Java two decades before. The man I had loved for more than half my life.

It was easy to find a taxi. Rental cars and taxis are everywhere the eye turns in Bali, with drivers hawking for customers from dawn till dusk. We chose the first rental car from a queue parked in front of the cafe. I left Angus to negotiate a price. He had excelled in Bahasa Indonesian at university and was competitive by nature. I felt shy about practicing the little I knew in his presence.

The whole winding way through the lush jungle scenery he laughed and joked and even sang Indonesian songs with the taxi driver but stayed silent with me, never showing any care, the way he once had. No sitting close. No holding hands. Barred from affection, while I swallowed tears and nursed a heart that felt savaged.

The acquisition of the beautiful white lace blouse, wrapped in layers of tissue and sprinkled with sweet frangipani flowers, and a silent flood of tears in the hotel bathroom later, were my only consolation. When life becomes too difficult to bear, we must always remember the small things of beauty in it.

I tossed the blouse onto the pile of things to give away, casting off the memories with it. The style would suit Harto's wife, Saraswati, I thought—its poignant history unsuspected. And she could have the fine-knit fuchsia-coloured cardigan too. The colour would match the shade of her favourite lipstick, and suit her wavy waist length hair, and the fair complexion she always protected so carefully from the sun. She always fretted about Harto's darker one.

"Don't forget to take a hat Harto," she would remind him, with a wife's loving frown, whenever he went outside to fly the small paper kites he made or fly the homing pigeons he kept in bamboo cages on the roof. "Ya, he would assure her with a gentle smile, but walk away bareheaded into the baking sun. His face and arms were always much darker than the rest of his body. "I don't care, he would whisper later in bed. My life and the blackness of my skin is my business." Harto kept his own council and followed his own stubborn heart.

Absorbed in all these thoughts, I continued to sort through the clothes. Hmm…how about this Japanese floral-patterned skirt for Saraswati too, I wondered. The wispy, cotton fabric would be cool in the tropical heat, and the Swiss voile lining soft on her skin. Yes. It would suit her very well, and I could make a similar one for myself later; especially now that my trusty Elna Lotus sewing machine and I had been reunited. Slipped through customs, with its pins and bobbins, via the cabin baggage allowance of my departing flight from Brisbane. I would have a good reason to look for fabrics in Yogyakarta, I thought, imagining the colourful rolls of cloth draped around dusty mannequins and spilling out of the stores in Jalan Malioboro and Jalan Solo.

As fate would have it, Saraswati and I both took the same dress size, a European small. Even our height was the same and the size of our feet. We had a few things in common besides Harto. And oddly enough we were both professional tailors, at home with tape measures slung around our necks, so that despite the limits of our conversation, we could spend happy hours together surrounded by the paraphernalia of dressmaking.

Galuh on the other hand had never sewn a stitch. She taught aerobics when the opportunity arose but mostly sold jelly drinks and *agar-agar* cakes from Leila's business. She too wore the same size as Saraswati and me, but the three of us could not have looked more different from each other. Both Saraswati and Galuh were pure

Javanese, from many generations back whereas I was born a third generation Australian of mixed but mainly European descent.

Perhaps my Irish ancestors were responsible for my hazel-green eyes and dark wavy hair, which appears, from a few steel-coloured strands, destined to soon turn silver-grey. My English forebears can be held to account for my pale skin that tans if I spend time in the sun but turns pale pink if the weather is cold. I suspect my Chinese ancestry may have influenced my average height and perhaps a French milliner aunt the mannequin's figure with which I was blessed. Not to boast, mind you, but rather to say we must be grateful for any small gift that life bestows.

My father always insisted that my square shoulders where due to his Welsh, Yeoman ancestors. He would pull his own broad shoulders back with pride as he said it, firing off an imaginary bow and arrow, to which as a little girl I would watch in wonder, my small pointy chin cupped in my hands. As far as I know I have a touch of Spanish blood too, which may account for a set of arched eyebrows, but no Italian, which does not explain my Roman nose.

If I could choose, I would have a neater, perter nose, like beautiful Saraswati, or Galuh, whose nose is much like Harto's—lineal and fine. At a glance the two could be mistaken for fraternal twins when in fact they are five years apart. Galuh is the older sibling, but cast from the same strong, masculine mould.

With these measures in mind, I threw a patch-pocket shirt with metal buttons onto Galuh's pile, and the baggy red T-shirt I had worn to school for Independence Day celebrations. Then again, I wondered if it might suit Harto better. He always looked striking in red.

These sartorial decisions were interrupted by a knock on the kitchen door. It was Pak Sungkar from the cottage across the road, with his ten-year-old daughter Yana. She was holding a fluffy white kitten to her chest—a source of comfort after losing her mother.

"Good evening, Miss Lara, how is your news? I have been talking with Harto. Would you like to accompany us to Yogyakarta tomorrow? I will take Yana to visit her cousins. They live in the central area not far from Bausasran."

"Hello Yana, how are you? I like your cat. Thank you, Pak Sungkar; I would appreciate it very much. What time will you set off?"

But of course, this simple exchange was in Indonesian, and I had to pretend I liked cats. It would have been heartless not to. Well, I don't mind cats from a distance and I quite like the bob-tailed ones in Java, especially the one that used to slink along the roofline with its bony shoulder blades in the afternoon, searching for rats. And I like the way cats yawn; and the way they can bring a stillness to the mind when you watch them lick their fur. But close up cats and longhaired dogs nearly always make me sneeze. That was one thing I had to tell Harto in the beginning because he is fond of all cats and dogs.

Aah...but wait...I am forgetting the rabid pack of dogs in Bali that upset his Javanese equilibrium—the ones with the missing tufts of hair that barked at his ankles and bared their canine teeth. The sharp-faced yellow dogs that awoke a fierce warrior in him who threatened to hurl stones until they thought better of it and slunk away, clamping their tufty tails between their spindly hind legs. It seems as if Bali is an island of gods and temples and gongs and dogs, and Java is a land of mosques and prayer calls—and a capital city full of nightclub temptations for men—and cats.

"Sleep early tonight Yana so you can surprise the sun," I said, pulling her and her white kitten cargo into a sideways hug. "Good night, Pak Sungkar. I hope you both sleep soundly."

"Sleep soundly too, Miss Lara," smiled Pak Sungkar "I will pick you up tomorrow morning after Subuh prayers.

5

The following morning, I was up and dressed in a comfortable pair of denim jeans and a loose white shirt with my hair pulled back into a high ponytail, before the dawn call to prayer crackled out from the gramophone speakers of the neighbourhood mosque. A fine mist from the dwindling contents of a bottle of Coco Chanel accompanied me from the bathroom into the cool living room air.

A late night had seen my suitcase crammed with clothes and standing on its wheels by the front door. A leather tote bag, sunglasses, lip balm, and a soft shawl were in a pile ready for departure on the Persian rug. There was a pair of tan leather slip-on shoes by the door, and I had an ear out for Pak Sungkar.

In the kitchen I lit the single blue gas burner and reheated some red rice porridge that Harto had prepared for me before he left. I could never make it as smoothly as he did. It all depended on the ratio of water and the way it was mixed. But there was more. "It is my responsibility," he would say, rolling out the first syllable of the six syllable English word. "It is my r-r-responsibility to look after you, while you are here in Java." And that is how smooth, red rice porridge took up a sentimental place in my diet.

Sitting on the kitchen step stool, I savoured a warm bowl of it topped with thin, liquid honey. As I rinsed the bowl, I caught sight of Pak Sungkar through the kitchen window. He was in his driveway loading an assortment of things into the boot of his white Toyota Kijang.

As an afterthought I threw some chocolate wafer snacks from the kitchen cupboard into my tote bag for the drive to Yogyakarta, and grabbed two salted duck eggs from the small fridge. I had forgotten to give them to Harto before he left. I placed them on a bamboo tray with a glass of sweet jasmine tea and took them out to Jamil.

Pak Jamil was the neighbourhood security guard, whose post just happened to be, most conveniently, located directly in front of the house.

"Good morning, Miss Lara, how is your news? When will Pak Harto come back?" he queried, dipping his head politely, as he raised his friendly caterpillar eyebrows into the furrowed lines of his forehead and reversed back, in his brass-buttoned uniform, onto a bench seat with the tray.

"I am going with Pak Sungkar and Yana now, to meet him in Yogyakarta. I think we may come back together on the train in a couple of days. Here are some extra rupiah, Pak Jamil, if you don't mind raking the leaves and trimming the hedges while I am away. Now that Aji has gone to work in Jakarta I can't ask him to help with garden chores anymore." And with that I pressed a roll of small rupiah notes into his palm.

"I'm very grateful Pak Jamil," I said, and I could see by his wide smile that he felt the same way and that these mutual favours, which had become a routine between us, warmed his days as much as mine.

"Thank you, Miss Lara, and please don't worry. I can organize everything for you. Nothing is a problem," he said, lifting the fly-deflecting lid from his glass before blowing the steam off his tea.

"Look, Pak Sungkar is coming now. Where is your bag, Miss Lara? I will carry it for you."

Jamil's actions were always as kind as his words, spoken in carefully enunciated Indonesian; a style that he and all the neighbours had adopted so considerately for me.

"Good morning, Pak Sungkar. Good morning, Yana, I call out. I hope you both had a refreshing sleep. Yana, where is your cat?"

"Yana's cat will travel in this special cage in the luggage compartment, Miss Lara," pipes out Pak Sungkar with a nicotine grin as he closes the boot of the Kijang before offering an early morning cigarette to Jamil and conversing a little with him in Javanese.

"Okay Yana, we can sit together on the back seat. Your cat is sure to enjoy her lazy time alone." And of course, I was relieved the fluffy white ball with the pink nose would not be sitting on Yana's lap.

"I have wafer snacks and games to play so we can enjoy the journey to Yogyakarta," I tell her with a chirpy school-teacher smile and show her a library bag filled with children's books, squeaky plastic animal toys and a box of coloured pencils. But it won't be long before the hum of rubber tyres on asphalt lulls little Yana and the cat to sleep.

Dappled sunlight dancing on the windscreen prompts me to pull the soft shawl from my bag.

"Please use this to cover your eyes, Yana," I say, feeling happy for having remembered to pack such a versatile accessory—and feeling a sense of belonging in a country of women for whom carrying a scarf is second nature.

In Sidoarjo I had learned never to venture too far without one handy, especially after the day I taught an impromptu class at an Islamic girls' school and needed to find a headscarf in a hurry. The worried faces of the front desk staff who welcomed me had said it was the rule for students during school hours so the teachers must follow. Then, there was a time I had to go on short notice into a mosque in Jakarta to speak with the Imam about a relative's wedding.

But in any case, I found the colourful scarves at the markets hard to resist; especially the printed silk ones and the woven ones from the Middle East—like the fringed, turquoise and orange tribal-patterned one that was draped over Yana's eyes as we drove. Another accessory to add to the little Jilbab headscarf she was wearing that day—the popular style with a lace and elastic border that fits around the face like a bonnet. She looked as demure and as devoted to Allah as her mother had been.

"How is everything in the back," Miss Lara, I hear Pak Sungkar ask, clearing a smoker's frog from his early morning voice. "Very comfortable thank you, Pak, but where is the seatbelt?"

"There are no seatbelts in the back, Miss Lara," he chuckles in apology.

"Forgive my rudeness, Pak Sungkar, it's just that I'm used to seatbelts in Australia."

In fact, I knew there were rarely seatbelts in the back seats of cars in Indonesia, but I asked anyway as a conversation starter. Pak Sungkar was a lawyer and might be interested in comparing notes about the different laws.

"Indonesia doesn't have a law for seatbelts in the back yet, Miss Lara. Only the driver must wear one."

"The road rules are very different here too, Pak Sungkar," I respond to the reflection of his receding hairline in the mirror, as he stretches the only seatbelt in the car over his shoulder and snaps the buckle into place.

"The rules make me so confused. I think it would be dangerous for everyone on the road if I attempted to drive here," I add, searching the floor for some space beside a slab of plastic aqua cups to comfortably rest my feet.

"I'm very happy to drive you to Yogyakarta, Miss, and so is Yana," says Pak Sungkar, backing out of the driveway and onto the street—all of us nodding and waving a friendly goodbye to Jamil as we pass.

"Please relax and enjoy the journey, Miss Lara. I am very familiar with the road to Yogya. I have driven there and back many times to visit my wife Ira's older sister."

"The same sister who came to visit last year, Pak Sungkar? The one who made the delicious *gulai* curry?"

"Ya, Tante Sarmini. You have a very good memory, Miss Lara."

"Both her kindness and her cooking are unforgettable, Pak Sungkar. One day I must meet her again to learn the recipe. What do you think, Yana?"

"Ya Miss, I hope for the same," she answers, muffling a yawn.

The warmth of this simple conversation in a mix of each other's languages seemed to have a magic wand effect, which eased my mind as we left the small streets of central Sidoarjo behind, and merged into the sea of traffic swishing back and forth on the busy Gempol Toll Road.

6

"We will pass Lapindo mudflow before long, Miss Lara," I hear Pak Sungkar say above the radio music. "There is already a strong smell of gas," he says winding up his window.

"Ah yes, I can smell it now too, Pak Sungkar," I say pulling up a corner of the shawl to cover my nose and mouth, careful not to disturb Yana, whose lace-trimmed head has nodded off to sleep.

"I've yet to see the mud, Pak Sungkar, and though Harto has frequently travelled this road he hasn't mentioned it at all."

"That is the Indonesian character, Miss Lara. Our focus is always on feeding our families regardless of the constant landslides, earthquakes and volcanic disruptions."

"That is true Pak Sungkar. Harto's focus has been on getting his wages home."

"Harto is a good family man, Miss Lara. You are fortunate to have his sincere help."

"Yes, Pak Sungkar, his instinct for protecting the people in his care is strong. The same cannot be said for the owner of the Lapindo mining company."

"Ya, Miss Lara. Lapindo have refused to take responsibility."

Fifteen minutes later, on the outskirts of Sidoarjo regency, the sailing traffic begins to beep and brake and weave itself into a creeping crawl. The road becomes bumpy and begins to jolt us around the car from back-to-front and side-to-side.

Suddenly a vast area of sunken houses comes into view. Whole neighbourhoods submerged. The only evidence of their former existence are the red-tiled rooftops peaking out above the sludgy slate-grey surface. It's the first time I'm seeing what I've heard so much about. What those with a television set would have seen if they watched the world news on 28 May 2006. News that an underground volcano had begun oozing mud in Java, and, like a strange beast, was belching the contents of its stomach on a half-hourly basis.

In Sidoarjo the neighbours were saying that a railway track had been submerged but Pak Sungkar says they mean the train line to Malang, not Yogyakarta. I relax back in my seat feeling selfishly relieved to know the way back on the Argo Wilis train with Harto, has so far not been impeded.

On the left there is mud as far as the eye can see. On the right markets and makeshift dwellings, a few sellers and customers dotted around, some streetside shops and garages still trying to function around all the roadwork and detour signs and road workers in sludge-covered yellow boots. The smell of methane gas hangs heavily in the air.

The road in front of us is completely covered with mud, crisscrossed with all kinds of tyre tracks. We slowly add ours to the mix, as Pak Sungkar pauses his friendly conversation and begins to focus the crease in his forehead on finding the right way out. Neither Yana, nor the cat stir.

All I can think of are the destitute families, but more especially the family of Lundy, a local teacher whose desk is beside mine at school. Her family's home had been swallowed by the mudflow. They were fighting for compensation the whole year that we worked together. In the meantime, she was living with relatives in Sidoarjo.

"Never mind. That's life. And anyway, some things are better," she would say with a half-smiling sigh of resignation—like the fact that she was closer to work and no longer had to commute in her clackety old Toyota Kijang. And with that she would break into peals of laughter as if she'd won a small lottery.

"My family might get a better house if the class action wins in court," she'd say, swinging around on her swivel chair and offering as usual to help me with my lesson plans.

And there in a nutshell is one of the things I love about the Indonesian character; that ability to be optimistic under the most difficult circumstances. A quality I needed more of in myself.

Lundy would one day tell me, very sternly, that I deserved much better things in my life. "Why do you settle for less Lara?" she would admonish.

But what did she know about me to say it? Well, we had each other's ear for almost a year and I can tell you now, we knew more of each other's secrets than most. Still, those words of hers left a sting that lasted, as the truth we hide from ourselves often does.

Never mind, we can only live one day at a time, and that day I was driving in the good company of Pak Sungkar and his small daughter Yana to Yogyakarta, and seeing misfortune far worse than mine.

"Yana is beginning to wake up Pak, because of the bumps. If she sees the sunken houses she might have bad dreams later."

"We will join the highway again soon, Miss Lara, and please don't worry about Yana. She has already seen the mud before. I told her all the people are safe and have new houses. She trusts my story," he says, throwing a doting glance back at his half-orphaned sleeping daughter.

"I hope that story comes true for the displaced residents, Pak Sungkar." But we both knew there was little chance. The residents were not only stuck in the mud, they were stuck between a mining magnate and Mother Nature's wrath. Some experts were blaming the massive earthquake that struck Yogyakarta two days before the mud began to pour out in Sidoarjo, 260 kilometres further east. Others said the mud volcano was triggered by a gas blowout from the pressure of giant drills. They say the fight for justice will take years and the mudflow could go on unabated for decades.

We trail along behind a clunky, mud-spluttered truck back onto the highway, leaving the vast mud lake behind. The truck is carrying a load of bricks and bags of cement tied to its long tray with ropes. There are three labourers in ragged clothes and rubber work boots perched on top. Two of them are leather-skinned and wiry, the third one taller, baby-faced and handsome with wide cheekbones that remind me of Aji. I pull my small digital camera out and lean forward to steal a photo. The young man flashes a shy smile and turns away to his friends.

"He looks similar to Aji, Miss. Have you heard any news from him?"

"Not yet Pak, not since he took the job in Jakarta. I hope everything is going well for him."

The stretch of single lane highway from the site of the mudflow to Yogyakarta turns into a pulsating vein of traffic, which takes most of Pak Sungkar's attention. It seems that he and every other driver on the road are intent on overtaking. I press my fingertips firmly into the edge of the vinyl seat, fixing my eyes on the road ahead. Driving is not as relaxing as the train ride, which I prefer, and where the odds of survival seem so much better.

As soon as Pak Sungkar sees an opportunity he speeds up and roars past the truck, leaving the bricks, cement bags and workmen in their billowing shirts behind. I hold my breath for all the long seconds we stay on the wrong side of the road. From there, Pak Sungkar's pattern of overtaking trucks and any other vehicles in his path on the way to Yogyakarta, and my breathing pattern, continues in a similar rhythm.

The trucks come in all shapes and sizes but have one thing in common. Each one is fitted with a blaring horn, and diesel engines that hiss and puff out plumes of greasy, black smoke.

Some of the trucks are carrying livestock; either cattle or goats crammed in together, or cages of clucking white-feathered chickens, which, Pak Sungkar and I decide, by their uniform size, are probably destined for Kentucky Fried Chicken.

Once again, I am relieved to have the scarf to cover my mouth and nose whenever the acrid smell of animal dung wafts in through the vents and mixes into the cool air-conditioned cab.

My approach is more discreet than Pak Sungkar's who, with each waft, winds down his window and spits out the sour smell, as so many men in Indonesia do though well-mannered in every other respect.

Mingled with the trucks there are tourist coaches and mini-vans crammed with passengers—and drivers with impossible deadlines to keep—and motorbikes that dart in and out of every other vehicle like flies, with riders in flimsy helmets and bandanas tied around their faces like cartoon bandits. Some of the women riders wear fingerless gloves or grip the handlebars from underneath to protect their skin from the sun, or wear cardigans in reverse, pulling the sleeves well down over their hands. Most wear pretty shoes.

As Pak Sungkar sails past, I see many young men whose only foot protection is often just a pair of rubber flip-flops. Their naked toes look vulnerable and cause me to drift into thoughts of Aji—his handsome face and the splayed toes of his rice farming feet—and the night that Harto took him to the bus station in Surabaya to catch an overnight coach to Jakarta.

He was wearing a pair of army boots that Harto had helped him to find in Surabaya. Sturdy second-hand ones made from matt-black leather. Harto had an eye for finding good quality used goods. He was skilled at surviving on little and Aji was keen to learn as much as he could in that regard.

Aji dreamed of finding his fortune in the neon lights of the capital. An acquaintance had lured him to work on a construction site there, along with a small group of labourers from Sidoarjo. I hoped the concrete jungle was treating them well, but I had my doubts.

Aji had been raised in a rural landscape just like the one we were travelling through that day. A green and gold landscape brushed with fertile rice paddies; dotted with farmers in coolie hats and water buffalo ploughing up slippery sods of soil. On the side of the road the occasional goat or cow could be seen grazing peacefully on tufts of grass, or weeds, or rubbish, seemingly oblivious to all the noise on the highway streaming past.

7

A distant memory filters through the landscape and fumes of diesel smoke. I'm on a bus to the port city of Semarang in the north of Java with Angus. We are in our early twenties. All the windows of the bus are open and sticky black smog is clinging to the sweat on our faces. There's a mini-bus in front of us with two floppy-eared brown goats roped onto the roof racks. Angus is practicing Indonesian with me from a pocket phrasebook, endearing the locals sitting in the seat behind us.

"The letter 'c' is always the same in Indonesian," he says. "It sounds like the 'ch' sound in chair. The 'a' sound is always the same too, he says, like the 'a' sound in far." He's quick to learn. I learn from him. The locals approve with toothy smiles and thumbs up. *"Bagus sekali,"* they say, swaying back and forth in their seats. "Very good. Very good."

The bus was stampeding along the twisting, single-lane highway with all its windows down when a tall red rooster made a suicidal dash across the traffic. The poor bird found itself witless in the middle of the road with its emerald-tipped feathers flapping to a percussive orchestra of horns, the most deafening and prolonged from our driver. Somehow the rooster managed to collect its feathers and strut safely back to the side of the road, though rather indignantly.

Pak Sungkar managed to avoid any such feathered friends on the road to Yogyakarta that day, but halfway between the mudflow and the city of Madiun he almost struck a cat.

The stray cat appeared as if from nowhere causing him to swerve suddenly into the path of oncoming traffic, and for me to remember the list of all my loved ones in what could have been a final prayer.

"Forgive me, Miss Lara, I had to swerve in order to avoid the cat," says Pak Sungkar, pulling a tissue from the box on the dashboard and wiping the beads of sweat running down his neck.

"No need to apologise at all Pak Sungkar. Your good driving saved us, and also saved the cat," I assure him, wiping my own brow. A little further on he told me something mysterious I hadn't heard before about cats in Java.

"We are lucky the goats are tethered, Miss Lara, and the cows are unlikely to stray, but cats like to roam and so can be unpredictable," he says, having composed himself again after the near collision.

"Yes Pak Sungkar, that is true, but I thought cats hunted at night."

"Usually Miss, unless they are suffering hunger and cannot wait for darkness to fall. Or if (and here he hushed his voice) they are possessed by a ghost."

"But how about Yana's cat, Pak Sungkar? Does it house an evil spirit too?"

"Yana's cat will let us know by her 'meow' if there are any evil spirits close by," he answers, in a low conspiratorial tone that will not alert Yana. "One or two meows are okay for a cat. Any more than that and it can sound like a baby's cry. That is evidence an evil spirit has entered. But we love cats because they can warn us and protect us from ghosts," he continued with a low chuckle.

"I'm sure I will look at cats more suspiciously now, Pak Sungkar."

"Ya, Miss, we must be careful because if we accidentally kill a cat, or even come across a dead cat somewhere, we must stop to pick it up and wrap it in something white, usually from our clothing. We must dig a hole to bury it and then pray," he adds. "It can take much time, Miss Lara."

"But how about if you are not wearing any white clothes, Pak Sungkar," I ask leaning further forward.

"That is far more inconvenient, Miss Lara. If we are not wearing anything white, we have to find something, like a towel or perhaps a sheet."

"Is it very unlucky if you don't bury the dead cat, Pak Sungkar?"

"Ya, Miss, we believe cats and other soft creatures like snakes can harbour ghosts. We must say a special prayer to ask forgiveness."

"Ah, I see, Pak," I nod, but I don't fully understand and make a mental note to ask Harto for some clarification later; especially about the snakes as we'd had a serious problem with cobras at the house in Sidoarjo when we first arrived.

"Soft creatures are easy for Satan to enter, Miss Lara, especially after dark. We believe that babies are vulnerable too. That's why we never take babies out early in the morning, or after dusk."

"That's interesting Pak Sungkar, I didn't know any of this before," I say, feeling a small window into the superstitious world of Indonesia opening another sunlit crack.

"We must be careful with Yana's cat then, Pak Sungkar. She is so attached to it."

"Ya, Miss Lara, her cat must be kept inside."

"How far to Madiun, Pak?" I ask, as Yana begins to rub her eyes. "We may need to stop for some food, and to use the rest room soon. And please let me fill the car with petrol." Though I said *bensin* instead of petrol, because we were mixing English and Indonesian together like an *oseng-oseng* stir-fry.

"That isn't necessary at all, Miss Lara; I will pay for the bensin. We are almost to Madiun—more than half way to Yogyakarta."

Knowing it is the custom to refuse an offer at least once I pull some rupiah notes from my wallet and put them on the console. I joke telling him it is a custom in Australia but not as weighty as the one he has just told me about cats, just a polite custom that I learned from my parents and must respect.

"Terima kasih banyak, Miss Lara," he answers nodding his nicotine smile into the rear-view mirror. "Thank you, Miss Lara, thank you very much.

8

As if these stories of wandering spirits, the smell of methane gas and diesel fumes—and the odour of animals in trucks on their way to slaughter—wasn't enough, Yana's cat in the back was starting to smell like pee. Some fresh air and some coffee sounded good, and after more than three hours my legs were stiff and needed to stretch.

I fished for a cup of water from a stash beside my feet and pierced the plastic lid with a sharp straw for Yana. She sucked in a long glazy-eyed sip.

"Soon we will stop for some food, Yana. Are you hungry?"

"*Sedikit*, Miss Lara," she mouths shyly. Just a little.

"Let's look for the sign that says Madiun, Yana. The first one to see it will be the winner," I say, retrieving her sandals from the floor and fastening them onto her feet.

"There is the sign for Madiun, Miss."

"Hooray! You are the winner Yana. I see you are fully awake. Your eyes are as sharp as an eagle." Even though we didn't really need the sign. The motorbikes parked on angles all along the curbs of the main street signalled that we had reached a city, but children like to be engaged in games.

"Yana is very clever, Pak Sungkar."

"Ya, Miss Lara, Yana is always a big help to her Papa," he agrees dotingly.

"Can you see the big restaurant over there, Yana," he adds, searching for her face in the rear-view mirror.

"We will stop for some food and a short rest. How about we buy some fried kampung chicken for your cat?" he adds, with a gentle father's love.

"Thank you, Papa; I think my cat is hungry," says Yana, her eyes opening wider at the prospect of feeding the fluffy white ball with the pink nose. And as if the cat can hear it twitches an ear and begins to lick a paw.

We pull into the restaurant, which is more of a giant roadhouse for travellers. Tourist coaches are spilling passengers out of their doors as we make our way across the car park. Most are women wearing headscarves and long skirts or dresses in mainly muted shades, contrasting with the tropical scene. They greet us with smiles of delight and approval at the sweetness of Yana wearing her jilbab. I ask one of them where the rest rooms are and she kindly shows us the way.

"You will have to pay one thousand rupiah to use it, Miss," she says in fluent English as she fishes in her wallet and pulls out a rupiah note to put in the wooden donation box for me.

With her flashing smile and thoughtful gesture, it's hard to refuse. One thousand rupiah is a tiny amount—enough to buy a box of matches—but small acts of kindness like these are worth a fortune.

Using a public toilet in Indonesia can be tricky business, mainly due to the floors being wet and slippery and the fact that people wash with water and a lather of soap rather than using paper. One fear is that using tissue paper isn't as clean as washing; the other is that the Dutch left such a poor sewerage system behind it would never cope with the paper waste. But in any case, it is quite an art to keep your clothes lifted from the floor and dry.

After hitching up Yana's long skirt and tucking it into the waistband I send her into a cubicle with a motherly warning to wait for me before she goes into the restaurant.

"There is a nasty smell, Miss Lara," she says, screwing up her button nose like a rabbit.

"Pinch your nose, Yana. Public toilets usually smell bad," I say through my own held breath, as I roll up my jeans and swap my leather shoes for the communal pair of rubber flip-flops outside the door. "Be brave like your favourite cartoon character, Dora the Explorer!" I tease.

I fasten the flimsy tin door behind me with the rusty latch and squint around for somewhere to hang my bag, being careful not to slide on the wet floor. Like a miracle a bent nail appears sticking out of the far wall. It will serve the purpose. Someone has left the tap on, as is often the way, and water is spilling over the top of a grimy, green plastic bucket.

The sound of splashing water being ladled with a plastic *gayung* signals a traditional Indonesian bathroom in use. Long gone are the days when these ladles were made from coconut shells. Those are only seen in boutique hotels selling nostalgia now. Occasionally there will be a modern flushing system, and that is often the case these days in wealthier circumstances, but it wasn't on the day we stopped in Madiun. The toilets were the traditional *jongkok* squatting style still seen in many homes.

Some might imagine I would turn my nose up at this situation, but they would be sorely mistaken. As with any place we love we can look past its faults and so for me, despite these rudimentary facilities, there was a certain romanticism that reminded me I was in a foreign country, and that I had escaped—at least for a while—from the grief that clung around me. And, that despite the smell, what I found disturbing wasn't the effluent of the masses in the world; it was the privilege and affluence of the few.

I shake my slightly soapy hands dry and collect Yana. By then it's late morning, and even though the dry season is coming to an end the day is steaming hot. We walk across the tarmac, around the resting tourist coaches, and pass a couple of orange-vested parking attendants who are busy protecting a row of motorbike seats from the midday sun with flattened cardboard boxes. Their brown faces are beaded with sweat and out of the air-conditioned car my linen shirt has begun to stick.

"Come on Yana, let's look for your Papa. You must be hungry by now," I smile, squeezing her hand as we trudge up the concrete steps and through the big entrance to the cavernous roadhouse.

A gaggle of noise greets us. There are people everywhere. Some standing in a line at the counter; others filling long rows of tables covered with orange plastic cloths and set with laminated menus; in the middle are plastic biscuit containers filled with homemade peanut snacks and krupuk crackers. A few dusty wall fans are doing their best to whisk away the stifling heat.

Emanating from speakers somewhere is the recorded cassette sound of *campursari*, the Javanese equivalent of country music embraced by the masses. The music combines string instruments with the xylophone sounds of traditional gamelan and flute. Sometimes it is slow and sultry, sometimes high-pitched, building up in tempo like a merry-go-round at a fair. The Javanese lyrics croon about everyday life or lost love and there's a dominant vowel sound like the double O in door. It's the same music that has been playing on the radio in the car since we left Sidoarjo.

Sopo sing kuat ditinggal lungo
Sopo sing atine ora loro
Kenangan sing wis tak lakoni
Tak simpen ning njero ati

Who can bear being left alone
Whose heart doesn't ache
All the memories I faced
Are still locked inside my heart.

Yana catches sight of her father as he stands to wave above the crowd of diners, whose plates are piled high with rice and spicy side dishes. She lets go of my hand and skips over to join him. He has already filled a large plate with fried tempeh and tahu, and a bony kampung chicken, and is busily brushing away the flies.

"Thank you, Pak Sungkar. Would you like some rice?"

"Not for me, Miss Lara, I have to be careful of diabetes," he answers, patting his round belly. "The doctor has told me to avoid rice for the moment, but please take some for yourself and Yana," he adds, indicating the restaurant-sized rice cooker on the counter that could surely feed a whole kampung.

"I'm sorry to hear that, Pak Sungkar. It must be difficult for you as an Indonesian," I say, taking a seat.

"Ya, very difficult Miss Lara, but never mind," he smiles, stubbing his clove cigarette into a melamine ashtray with no apparent concerns about lung disease.

"How about a happy soda, Yana," I suggest. "Let's go and choose one."

On the big board behind the counter there are pictures of colourful sodas filled with shaved ice and *agar-agar* jellies, all topped with scoops of coconut ice cream.

"How about the one with the pink syrup, Yana? The glass is so pretty like you."

"One or two, Miss," calls the seller.

"Just one for this sweet child here, Mbak."

"Thank you, Miss," says Yana, taking a sip of the sugar-loaded layers through a red plastic straw as she tiptoes daintily back to the table and attaches herself to her father's side.

"Have you eaten enough, Pak Sungkar? You will need your energy for driving."

"The strong coffee will keep me alert," he says, don't worry, Miss Lara.

"Yes, Pak Sungkar, the coffee here is very strong. It may keep us awake until midnight," I agree, and smile as I watch him make wide Balinese *kecak* dancer eyes for fun at Yana.

Not only is the coffee rich and dark and unfiltered; it's laced with a generous amount of treacle-tasting palm sugar.

"I will ask the staff to wrap the leftover chicken, Miss Lara. Please wait a moment," Pak Sungkar says, signalling to a group of waiters standing idle near the counter.

"Your cat will have a feast soon," I say, turning to Yana, who is swinging her legs in the seat beside me. "How is your happy soda? Your smile has grown bigger," I tease, as she blows soft bubbles with her straw into the sticky remains in her glass.

"Are you ready to feed your *harimau*," I ask her, emphasising the word harimau, because we had been playing 'match the animal' in the car earlier.

"Harimau is tiger, Miss. Cat is kucing."

"Oh, silly me, Yana. We will do another memory game on the way to Solo and some drawing too. But first, let's add the animal words to our list."

cat: *kucing*
dog: *anjing*
goat: *kambing*
tiger: *harimau*

"*Ayo*! Are we ready to continue our journey," asks Pak Sungkar, using the catchy term for 'come on' as he picks up the better part of a fried chicken the waiter has returned to him in a takeaway box.

"Yes, Pak Sungkar, but it will save time if I pay for our meal at the cashier desk while you and Yana look after the cat," I insist, looking for a way to help with expenses that can't be refused.

After Pak Sungkar's enlightening story, we can't risk letting Yana's much-loved cat out of the cage. She picks off some pieces of chicken to put inside it on a paper serviette. I can't be sure if the haughty meow that escapes from the fluffy white ball is a ghostly 'thank you' or purely feline, but either way it seems to chide us, saying, "Well, it's about time you people thought about my food."

While Yana feeds and whispers encouragement to her cat, Pak Sungkar inhales the last flickering drag of another clove cigarette.

By the time we pile back into the oven-warm car it's almost noon, and I'm wondering about Harto and the house he has found. In fact, I have been wondering about these things for most of the drive and hoping Bausasran will have the homely atmosphere I crave.

9

Harto and I had exchanged a few text messages along the way; tapping out the letters on the button keyboards of our silver Nokia phones. I wrote that we hadn't yet reached Solo—the royal sister city of Yogyakarta.

For the Javanese, these two cities are the centre of the known universe, and years before, Solo had been the centre of mine.

The city is cast with memories of my youth. The nine months I spent living there twenty-five years before had set the course my life would take—for better and for worse.

I check for text messages on my phone. There is one from Harto:

> Let me know when you pass
> Prambanan temple Lara

The ancient Hindu temple of Prambanan with its tall spires reaching for heaven was just a few kilometres out of Yogyakarta. Harto and I had often escaped to the gardens surrounding the temple compound in the weeks after we first met. The rolling gardens were rare green space, and a place where we could spend time together in the meditative stillness that pervades the grounds.

I hadn't seen Prambanan temple since the big earthquake that shook Yogyakarta to its knees the year before. Harto told me there had been damage to the spires and that some large stones had fallen. Since then, the site had been fenced off from the public and scaffolded for repairs.

There are many legends about Prambanan—as many as there are Hindu deities. But the story I remember most is the one that Harto told me the day we stumbled around the granite ruins of Candi Sewu temple; a short walk-through the weedy paths around the main temple.

Sewu means one thousand in Harto's first language of Javanese; the language in which of course he is the most proficient. There aren't really one thousand temples. There are more like two or three hundred, but legends like to exaggerate, and fantasies are often better than facts.

"I cannot tell you the history of Prambanan temple because I wasn't born, and I haven't studied," he joked, the first time he took me to see its grandeur. "But I can tell you the legend of a thousand temples, because my grandmother told me the story when I was a child."

"There was a prince who wanted to marry a beautiful princess," he began. "Her name was Roro Jonggrang. The prince was blinded by her beauty, but she would not accept him."

"Why not, Harto," I interrupted.

"Because she didn't like him, that's all," he replied, with an apologetic smile at the lack of detail.

"I beg your pardon, please continue, Harto," I said, cupping my chin in my hands, satisfied with this simple explanation. He flicked the grey ash from his clove cigarette onto the black sandy soil and cleared his throat.

"Actually, the prince had killed her father in a war, and she would not forgive him," he added.

"That is understandable Harto, no matter how handsome the prince may have been, a father's love can be the measure for any other man that follows." Harto agreed, rolling up the sleeves of his navy, cotton drill shirt and continued.

"In order to avoid a marriage she did not want, she gives the prince a job. She asks him to perform two impossible feats in one night. The first is to dig a deep well. The second is to build one thousand temples before sunrise the following day. She feels sure the prince will not succeed, but she is wrong. The prince called on some ghosts from the earth to help him."

"How many ghosts, Harto? Were there just one or two, or many?" Harto hesitated for a while, searching his memory for the story his grandmother had told him.

"There were one thousand ghosts," he said at last. "One for each temple. They had almost succeeded in building the thousand temples, all except for the last one. The dawn was approaching. It meant the ghosts would soon return to the earth," he said, breathing out a thoughtful stream of smoke. "The princess was becoming afraid, so she asked one of her ghosts to play a trick on the prince and his army of ghosts."

"Aah, so the princess had her own ghosts too, Harto?" I said, interrupting again.

"She was a powerful princess," he answered convincingly. "She asked her ghosts to make a sign that it was already morning so that the last temple could not be built in time."

And here Harto did not say 'asked' but rather 'organised' because he was making a chivalrous effort to tell the story, or at least part of it, in English, and languages don't always use the same expressions.

"So you are saying the princess organised her ghosts to wake the sun up early," I asked, amusing myself with the use of 'organise'.

"Something like that," he said, "and she also organised the people to start pounding rice before dawn to confuse the ghosts even more," he continued.

"What happened then," I asked, with no further questions about the fake sunrise.

"The prince could not control his anger," he said, "He turned Roro Jonggrang into stone."

"I prefer your story to the one the tourist guides tell," I say, gazing up at him as he sat on a hill of mossy granite stones that would have fallen into rubble centuries before. But what I really preferred was the magical setting with him in it, and the day surrounding us. The hazy heat and the lazy feel of it, under the vast powder-blue sky. And, it was in his telling of the story that he became a prince to me.

"I will call you *Pangeran* from now on," I said, teasing him. "In my story you are a handsome prince who has escaped from the Sultan's palace and lives secretly amongst the small people of kampung Surokarsan."

And forever after that I called him Pangeran H. Hartono, the first, or just Pang for short. Still, he accepted the title humbly, with just the hint of a dimpled smile, as he reached out his newly royal hand for mine, and pulled me up from the slope of the carved granite stone from where I had sat and listened. And in the bright light of day, we scrambled together across the rest of the ruins of a thousand temples to see the statue of Roro Jonggrang, still standing in Prambanan temple today.

10

That day in Prambanan had been as bright as the sun reflecting on the bonnet of Pak Sungkar's Kijang as we followed the road towards Harto—and as light as the campursari music playing on the radio.

"Would you like to read a story together," Yana, I ask, coming out of my reverie and pulling a picture book from the canvas bag of activities I have brought along for the drive.

"Look, the writing is in both English and Indonesian. We can learn some new words together," I say, opening the cover and thinking it will be a good way to pass the time until we reach Solo.

"We can take turns," I suggest, encouraging her in the schoolteacher way that had become a habit of mine with all children by then.

"I like the pictures very much, Miss," says Yana, leaning closer.

"Did you know this storybook is a gift for you, Yana? See, I have written your name here," I say, pointing out the inside cover with her name surrounded in hand-drawn hearts.

"Thank you, Miss Lara, I know this story from school," she tells me, her eyes bright.

And so, we begin to read the famous Indonesian fairy tale about two stepsisters: one of them good and one of them naughty. One of them is called *Bawang Merah*, which means red onion. The other sister is called *Bawang Putih*, which means white garlic. And as with fairy tales all over the world they are fables to teach children values, but unfairly as well, the good child is white. And just as in Cinderella, the stepmother is wicked, putting all stepmothers forever after in the same box with her.

"Shall we swap the sisters' names to different colours for fun," I suggest, after we finish reading. Yana nods a timid smile. So, for the rest of the way to Solo, we change all the colours of the characters. Their eyes become violet or green, and their skin, indigo or orange.

By the time we get to the outskirts of Solo, a small girl from East Java, riding in the back seat of her father's white Toyota Kijang with a recently qualified English teacher from Australia—and a precious, fluffy white cat—has memorised all the colours of the rainbow equally well in two languages:

red: *merah*
orange: *oranye*
yellow: *kuning*
green: *hijau*
blue: *biru*
indigo: *biru nila*
violet: *ungu*

And she had learned that stepmothers can be kind, because schoolteachers are trained to seize the teaching moments that arise, no matter how much effort has gone into a lesson plan.

Yana tucks her new storybook carefully into her pink and purple school satchel and leans over the back seat to check on her cat, contentedly curled up in its cage. Happily, all the chicken pieces are gone, leaving behind the triangle of paper tissue soaked in turmeric-yellow grease.

"I think your cat is saving its energy for catching *tikus* later tonight," I joke, "but if you give her some more ayam I'm sure she will stay with you instead," I add to smooth her sudden frown.

"Yana, we must add the English words for ayam and tikus to our list of animals."

"I know ayam already, Miss. Ayam is chicken."

"How about tikus?"

"Tikus is mouse. I know because sometimes Papa watches Tom and Jerry cartoons together with Uncle Harto and me." But she calls him *Om* for uncle, adding to the list of warm and respectful titles that must precede a person's name.

"Aah…so that is what they do while Miss Lara is working hard at school. Thank you for that information, Yana," I say, teasing her but feeling proud in the knowledge that two grown men have found a way of ensuring a motherless child feels secure and happy.

"You're right, Yana. A small tikus like Jerry is a mouse. A big one is a rat. Remind me to give you some silver-star stickers when we return to Sidoarjo.

"Miss, can we have a drawing competition, to see who can draw the funniest mouse?"

"Of course, Yana," I say, with a grin to match her sudden beam of enthusiasm. "But my mouse drawing skills are limited. I think you will win by a mile."

My mouse drawing skills were indeed limited, especially compared to the uninhibited artwork that only children can create, but my list of rat stories was not. I had encountered a few on my travels in Asia, most scurrying across roads or squashed in the middle. Once, in Singapore, I found myself sharing a hotel room with a little grey one. But the biggest rat I had ever seen was in Solo. The city we were fast approaching.

The rat resided in the roof of the guesthouse where I lived with Angus more than twenty years before. The guesthouse was set in the front garden of a large home in Jalan Ronggowarsito. Not far from Mangkunegaran, the sprawling royal palace.

The hairy rodent would cause quite a commotion whenever it scurried out of the roof cavity and ran along the partition separating one guest room from the other.

Sometimes it poked its head out of the garbage that had begun a malodourous wilt into compost in the concrete bins that lined the street. We knew whenever its whiskery nose made an appearance by the sudden flurry of action and panicked shouts, and the flip-flop sound of sandals running up and down the asphalt street.

Awas tikus! Awas tikus! Be careful of the rat! Be careful of the rat! But the rat would escape as usual, disappearing with its long tail, into the open drains.

In my memory I can still hear Siti, the housekeeper from next door, hurrying to everyone's rescue waving her worn-out millet broom. We are both gawking in disbelief at the four-legged fugitive on the run—our hearts beating as fast as her feisty domestic weapon can thump the ground. The rat was a freak of nature as big as a cat!

I remember how Siti laughed and squealed, and brushed its imaginary nipping teeth away from her ankles in horror. And how I latched onto her shoulder and brushed my ankles too, and how we fell about laughing—and I squealed louder.

I toy with the idea of entertaining Yana with the story but decide against it. Perhaps better to tell her the children's tale of the Pied Piper and the mice of Hamelin instead. Or recreate a verse!

Tick and tock
Tick and tock
Two mice ran up the clock
The clock struck two
And down they flew
Tick and tock
Tick and tock

11

Solo is full of memories of my past. They invade my thoughts like ripples on a murky pond, as Pak Sungkar begins to slow the wheels of the car and negotiate the roundabout that leads us into the more densely populated centre of Solo.

"Miss Lara, have you ever seen a traditional dance at the *keraton* just here," he asks, interrupting my thoughts as he glides the car past the grounds of Mangkunegaran Palace and we see the stately splendour of its white walls come into full view.

"Many times, Pak, when I lived here as a young woman. The house where I stayed was in the street of Jalan Ronggowarsito, very close to here. Perhaps we can visit Solo again to take Yana, or go to see the Ramayana ballet at Prambanan temple in the future."

"Inshallah, Miss Lara. I pray that may happen too," he says, nodding and swaying in his seat as the palace disappears from sight.

A moment later, Marion, my friend from Berkley, California, materializes in my mind's eye. She's coming through the big green gates of the same big house in Jalan Ronggowarsito for the first time.

I close my eyes and there she is with her big, deep-dimpled American smile. She is a tomboy in a pair of khaki trousers, lugging a heavy backpack. I am a feminine girl in a floral skirt.

I remember how crestfallen I felt at first, realizing that I would probably have to share the guesthouse I'd had to myself with Angus. But I remember how that feeling changed when I heard her play the piano in a music store on the main street. I was entranced. Her fingers tripped so lightly over the keys, transporting me into another world:

a world of clear mountain streams and fish slipping freely through the currents. Her talent, her warmth, her passion for life and her laugh, were infectious.

At the same time Marion became intrigued with me. With personal things like the fact that I used henna powder to shine my hair; and wore lipstick and eye shadow and waxed the hair off my legs.

"I'm from a family of girls, Marion, the middle sister of five; the daughter of a doting father and a dressmaker-mother with a movie star's figure for clothes. There was little chance of avoiding such feminine things, surrounded by mirrors and lipstick and powder and paint."

Our backgrounds were very different but we fitted together as perfectly two pieces of a jigsaw puzzle. She was an outdoor girl who had grown up hiking in the mountains of Colorado with grizzly bears for company. She had never thought of removing a single hair from her body. Never shaved an underarm or shaped an eyebrow. Still, she was eager to add these skills to her repertoire and we certainly had some fun in the process.

"This is really new for me," she would say with her big American smile as she held up the sticky wax strips, while I lay as her guinea pig on the four-poster mosquito-curtained bed. I remember how she told me, as she tore off the wax strips, that her sister would appreciate this help back home in The States.

In Singapore, I had managed to squeeze a few beauty supplies into the backpack I carried with me—and my heart's desire—a silk *cheongsam* dress from Chinatown. All slipped stealthily into my backpack while Angus was off photographing orchids with his big lens camera. He had insisted I carry a backpack if I wanted to join him on his spiritual journey—a crippling feat as the weight of mine increased.

In Solo, Marion became better company for me than Angus. And more fun than the Western attendees of the meditation group we had joined—an aloof group of spiritual searchers who failed to offer the same hand of friendship.

With Marion I was accepted without conditions. Those few months brimmed with happiness and laughter. At night we sang songs and practiced scales, while Angus was out, spreading his effervescence around others—the spark that had stolen my heart.

And it wasn't as if he missed me when Marion came along. In fact, the spring in his step increased with the sense of duty she took off his hands. After all he was an erudite young man held in high regard. It suited him well if I could find my own interests. Still, I craved desperately for his attention. Lived in the hope of it.

12

"Are you interested in looking for batik in Pasar Klewar, Miss," asks Pak Sungkar, reeling me out of my thoughts.

"Thank you for the offer, Pak Sungkar, but perhaps another time," I say, remembering the cavern of stifling heat and the corridors crammed with batik fabrics, and clothes, and handicrafts and haggling customers—and thinking it might all be too much for a tired ten-year-old girl who is missing her mother.

I fade back into my seat with Yana and back into my memories. There is Marion again in my mind's eye. We are making our first and only batik paintings in a *pendopo* somewhere around here. I can still see her dipping the waxed cloth into the inky boiling water. She's laughing, and it's contagious, and there is indigo dye all over her hands.

"Yana, can you see the wet batik fabrics hanging over the bamboo sticks. See in the front garden there," I say, spying a familiar courtyard. We are getting closer and closer to Jalan Ronggowarsito and it seems not much has changed in twenty years.

There are more new cars crowding the roads and mobile phone towers have popped up here and there; but the boldly painted *becak* pedicabs are still cruising the street and the smell of burning charcoal and open drains still permeates the air.

"Would you like to make a batik painting one day, Yana," I ask with an encouraging pinch of her cheek. She nods shyly as her little hands twist the colourful scarf we are sharing.

"Making batik is fun, like colouring, but much harder. You have to control the boiling wax with a special tool called a *tjanting*; and you have to be very patient."

--oOo--

I remember how the one and only batik tablecloth I ever made had blob marks in between the butterflies, but how Marion held it to her breast when I gave it to her as a parting gift. How she breathed in the wax smell as she climbed the steps of the bus to leave, and smiled, but not her big American smile—more the smile of a sister who shares the same blood. She said she would always cherish it.

We didn't cry when she left for Singapore, the first leg of her journey home, but I remember how empty I felt as I walked back from Jalan Selamat Riyadi without her, and her room was vacant, and her *tabla* drums were gone.

She taught me to play the small tabla drums that she had brought with her from her travels in India. And she taught me how to sing a high note because she knew the correct way to breathe.

Marion and I would sometimes jump out of bed with the dawn call to prayer. We would dress in a hurry and dash out to buy sweet mung bean porridge for breakfast from a passing peddler. Afterwards we would stroll to Pak Bambang's big house behind Pasar Klewar to learn yoga, but really so that she could stay on after the class to play her musical compositions on his baby grand piano.

I remember how she persuaded me to sing backing vocals for the recordings we made on the double cassette player Angus bought in Singapore. And I remember how she begged me to think deeply before I married him, and how I didn't listen.

"I'm sorry to say, Lara, but he's arrogant. And I don't appreciate his jokes about unattractive women. Does he see women as nothing more than sexual objects?"

"I agree he has a tendency to be arrogant, Marion, but he is well aware of his ego. The main reason for him being here is to contain it," I answer, defending him. "And as far as his attitude to women, he firmly believes in equality and the women's liberation movement. He even insists I keep my own surname when we marry. He says it's a woman's right."

"Has he given you a choice?" she asks, casting a dubious glance.

"He says I'd be stupid to take his name."

"Lara, that's enforced emancipation, not equality."

"You're wrong, Marion. He is a true feminist," I persist, refusing to acknowledge any faults in the man I will soon marry. Sometimes we have to learn things the hard way.

While Marion and I lived in Solo we always supported each other. One night, when she was reading in the guesthouse alone, the rat made a bid for freedom, running along the partition that separated her room from the one I shared with Angus. She fled down the street to find me sitting on a bench seat at the *susu warung*. Her face looked as pale as the milk drinks on the menu. We laughed about the rogue rat until we cried.

The guesthouse however, was far from a haven for rodents. Apart from the hairy old resident rat it was vermin free. In fact, it was part of a well-kept and elegant home surrounded by manicured gardens. The gardens had been created by an equally elegant Javanese man; a Buddhist convert and theosophist, with an aristocratic background and a pair of bookish glasses.

There was a Bodhi tree in the grounds behind the kitchen, and a moss-covered concrete well. Suspended on a thick rope above it was a tin bucket for drawing water. If you leaned over the side, you could see your reflection in the glassy pool below.

Angus and I had turned up eagerly at his house, one muggy mid-morning, with a copy of Bill Dalton's Indonesian Handbook. We had shown him a page with the address Jalan Ronggowarsito 60, and a paragraph about a form of Javanese, relaxation meditation. "Would this be the same address Sir, and would you happen to be the same Pak Suyono mentioned here?" we enquired, with wide, innocent eyes.

Pak Suyono was immediately engaging. With a ballet dancer's posture, he invited us with an outstretched arm into his library. We sat captivated on rattan chairs opposite him and listened as he shared his vision of bringing the spiritual teachings of the East and West together—his English as eloquent as an Oxford scholar.

We took note of the books on his shelves by authors we had read: Alice Bailey, Paramahansa Yogananda, Sai Baba, Gandhi, Aldous Huxley and Krishnamurti among them. Over the previous year Angus had accumulated a similar collection from the esoteric bookshelves of the Circle Bookshop in Brisbane.

I'm in the car with Pak Sungkar and Yana, but my thoughts are not. I'm in the library again behind the green gates of Pak Suyono's house. I look around the room. There isn't a speck of dust to be seen on the dark-stained, teak furniture. Not a brass doorknob nor glass-paned window left unpolished.

An elderly Javanese woman in traditional dress pads softly through a doorway carrying a wooden tray. She deposits three glasses of sweet jasmine tea onto a low table and crouching down on her haunches reverses out, her barefoot steps never making a sound.

Angus is full of questions on spirituality. Two intelligent minds and both have a gift for deep discussion. I am more an observer, struggling with my religious bent. Torn between the Catholic upbringing I had recently abandoned and the New Age movement of my generation.

Young people like us had been leaving behind their Christian upbringings in droves, blazing trails to India in search of Hindu gurus and ashrams, or to Nepal in search of Buddhist monks and nirvana–
–searching for themselves. They questioned the concept of heaven, hell and purgatory; read books by Carlos Castenada and Timothy Leary and some took psychedelic drugs.

The New Age movement came with its own set of vocabulary: karma, kundalini, chakras and pranayama, and the promise of a utopian world where love and peace prevailed. A world in which complete strangers would gaze into each other's eyes and become one with the cosmic vibration of the universe. It was the harbinger of holistic diets and homeopathic medicine, of herbal teas and Bach flower remedies. Many would be inspired to follow a strictly vegetarian diet, which favoured linseed, alfalfa sprouts and lentil burgers, and frowned upon the meat and boiled vegetables parents had dished up at the dinner table, and the sliced white sandwich bread taken to school for lunch.

In 1978, we were at the tail end of the hippie movement on our way through Southeast Asia on a shoestring budget, though we didn't quite fit the mould. We both failed to follow the hippie backpackers' relaxed rules of dress. Angus was the son of a high-ranking soldier who had ruled his family with military discipline. I was a dressmaker's daughter who preferred silk chiffon to cheesecloth, and we both preferred our travel wardrobes freshly laundered and ironed. In that regard we were as neat in appearance as Pak Ananda Suyono Hamongdarsono—the man we had just had the pleasure of meeting.

We step out of the library into the daylight and follow him around the sculpted gardens. I am watching his movements again, as graceful as a swan. He's dressed in a cool-grey checked sarong, and a crisp-white-cotton Nehru collared shirt. Later he tells us that as a young man he went on a yearlong pilgrimage to India and that he once fasted on nothing but young coconut water for forty days.

His image is as clear in my mind as the day we met. His hair is impeccably combed back, receding and painted black, his pale, amber skin smells of jasmine soap. He looks to be in his mid-forties.

"There is a *paranormal* teacher in Kampung Sewu," he tells us. "We can visit him one day if you have time. He may be able to help you with your dharma—your path in life." We look at him in wonder and glance at each other. We are a picture of youth and dharma, not yet lived. It is the late seventies and we have unexpectedly stumbled onto a Javanese path to spiritual enlightenment.

Afterwards I hear Angus say excitedly, "I'm not going to India; I will stop here for six months instead. It's up to you if you want to follow." And of course, I stay, and for a while I follow, because ever since the day we first met I have found it hard to be without him.

But I'm not comfortable with all the Western meditators; they are so full of confidence and clever questions. Two weeks later I take an overnight bus to Kuta Beach in Bali, buy a batik string bikini, and spend three weeks on the white sand meditating on the waves instead.

I'm sad and my appetite has gone. Inside is hollow. I think we have separated. But one morning he appears at the losmen where I'm staying. Appears with his ocean big eyes—out of the blue. Turns up unexpectedly with his fresh-faced smile and his lush, dark, wavy hair. He takes me to bed. Then I think we are still together. But later he says he was just checking that I am okay. Now I'm missing him more, and I'm all mixed up. I think I need some space.

"We both need some space," I say. I'm only twenty-one and I'm homesick. I fly back to Sydney alone.

--oOo--

For six months Angus sends weekly letters about his spiritual progress. He still calls me 'Babe' and tells me how much he misses me. So, then I think that we haven't broken up after all. I post weekly letters back. Less than a year later we are in Solo again together as special guests of Pak Suyono.

Angus tells me that after all the soul-repairing months without me, the meditation sessions with special guides, and lengthy discussions about life with Pak Suyono, he is now ready to marry. We sleep in each other's arms. I feel warm and loved. I feel like the chosen one.

We stroll blissfully around the gardens. He introduces me to a young married couple he knows well by then. They are Pak Suyono's housekeeping staff of two. The woman has a bald-headed baby strapped to her hip with a batik *selendang* papoose. She is sweeping the yard. Her husband is on his way out to run errands.

"Pak Suyono wants to keep the couple together," states Angus proudly. "Poorer families are often separated by the need to work in different cities to survive," he adds, with an air of authority on the subject—an air that as he has on a vast range of subjects; and the authority of a gifted student who has thrice been dux of his school.

"Pak Suyono, like you, is a very different thinker to most, Angus," I say adoringly, reading too much into the comment about the importance of couples staying together.

As Pak Sungkar turns the corner into Jalan Ronggowarsito I wonder if Pak Suyono is still alive. If so, he must by now be in his mid-seventies.

13

"Pak Sungkar, there is the house where I used to live when I was young," I say, but more to myself, as we round the corner into Jalan Ronggowarsito. "Do you mind if we stop for a moment? I'm curious to see if the owner Pak Suyono still lives there."

"Please go ahead, Miss Lara, I will wait here with Yana," he says, pulling over to the side of the road. As he brakes, I notice the big green gates to the house are shut.

"Thank you, Pak Sungkar," I say, and to Yana more brightly. "I'll be back soon. How about you play with your cat?"

I pull the long *kerudung* scarf around my shoulders and partly over my head, though it isn't necessary or expected of a Western woman. It's more for the sense of security a scarf can offer and the touch of finery a length of beautiful fabric can add to an outfit. But on top of all that, a sign of formality at the house with the big green gates would be respectful.

Head coverings were seldom seen on women in the street twenty-five years before. Of course, the white *mukena* or a kerudung was always worn to the mosque, and that remains the same. But religious fashions had vastly changed in Java during my years away. By the time I returned, many Muslim women had embraced the jilbab so that the whole society, especially in East Java, appeared more like Malaysia.

Kerudung were—and still are—worn as part of traditional Javanese dress. They are worn draped over the shoulders of women dressed in fitted kebaya blouses, and wrapped in lengths of stiff batik *kain* that allow only for the smallest of steps to be taken in their dainty bejewelled slippers. Their hair is swept up into elaborate *sanggul* buns spangled with gold. This traditional dress is worn for special events. One January night in 1981 women so dressed made up the host of feminine guests who attended my Javanese wedding—held in the garden pavilion of Pak Suyono's elegant home.

"I won't be long, Pak Sungkar," I say, feeling my nerves rising. I'm revisiting a past that was scattered with important people on intellectual and spiritual pursuits, and where I have to confess, I often felt like an imposter.

The sun is beginning to cast mid-afternoon shadows as I cross the narrow street. A woman in a *daster* housedress is sweeping her front yard one-handedly with a coconut-palm broom. Her left arm rests on the small of her back, in the customary way that she would have been taught as a girl. She nods a friendly smile.

A young man sprinkles water from a bucket with his cupped hand onto the road—helping to turn down the heat one degree. A pedicab is parked lazily under a shady tree. Tendrils of clove-scented smoke are drifting from a cigarette dangling between the brown, wrinkled fingers of the driver's hand. He's half asleep under his bamboo fisherman's hat, which is painted turquoise blue. I notice a faint smell of sandalwood incense in the air, surely emanating from behind the big green gates.

I knock gently. No answer. I knock again more firmly. Still, no sign of life.

"Do you know if Pak Suyono is still living here?" I ask an old woman who is selling jamu herbal drinks nearby.

"*Maaf, Mbak, ngakk tahu*," I'm sorry Missis, I do not know, she answers, with a toothy smile and skin as fine as silk satin, stretched across her wide cheek bones.

"Mau beli jamu, Missis?" she offers, as a consolation and to make a sale of course.

"Can you wait for a moment, Ibu? I want to stay here a few minutes longer in case someone comes to the door."

I knock again a few times and hear the shuffle of feet. The gate creaks and opens a crack and to my surprise a Western woman, who looks to be in her mid-forties, appears. She's dressed in traditional Javanese clothes: a tightly wrapped batik sarong and a yellow lace kebaya. Her hair is blond. She looks me over with a somewhat suspicious eye and musters a tiny smile.

"Pak Suyono is not holding meditation sessions for now," she says, guarding the house and gardens from my curious gaze.

"I'm not here for meditation," I say, in a friendly tone. "I was married here years ago in the pendopo and would like to give my regards to Pak Suyono if you don't mind. I am just passing through with some friends on the way to Yogyakarta, and this opportunity may not happen again."

"I'm sorry, Madame, but I can't let you in. Pak Suyono has retreated from the world for now," she says, with an accent that sounds German.

"I understand," I say. "He gave so much of his time to others. I'm happy to hear he's taking some time for himself, but could you let him know that I called in to say hello," I insist, scribbling my name on a page from the notepad I have pulled from my brown leather bag. But then I wonder if Pak Suyono will remember my name, so I add Angus.

"My husband was very close to Pak Suyono," I say "He treated him just as a son."

She gives a disinterested smile and starts to push the big, green gate closed.

"But wait! Please wait just a moment," I say, adjusting my scarf. "Could you give him my best...and...and...could you tell him our son, Amar, whose name he chose has all grown up...and...and...and he's finished school...and...and...can you say, I hope his son, Wibowo, is healthy and doing well."

Still my words held no sway. They seemed of little importance. She took the note and folded it into her hands, which for the whole time had been held together in the Buddhist manner of prayer. Then she gave me a Buddhist bow of piety and slowly closed the big green gate. Closed the gate on my memories of a house and a garden and a well and the world of a scholar with a library of New Age books.

To many people in the world, Pak Suyono was a leading light for Sumarah, the practice of sujud or total surrender in meditation—a spiritual teacher and scholar with a dream of bringing the East and West together. Each person who knew him will have his or her story, as I have mine, and each story as special.

For me, Pak Suyono will always be the generous man who opened the green gates of his home in friendship and arranged my wedding in the cool pendopo of it—to the young man I loved.

I wonder if she knew that some bonds can never be broken and that the green gate was no barrier, though it would have been wonderful to see him all these years later.

Pak Ananda Suyono Hamongdarsono resided not only behind the green gates in Jalan Ronggowarsito; I carried him and his words of wisdom in my heart.

The only thing that is permanent is impermanence, he taught me once, and I have learned it well. For years I kept a word he had written in large letters on a piece of paper, and the word was—BE. And I read, and read, and read again, the Krishnamurti book that he gave to us as a parting gift.

14

The jamu seller has waited patiently, squatting beside her heavy bamboo basket, which is crammed full of glass-bottled herbal concoctions. I stroll over and squat beside her with a weary smile and ask for suggestions.

"I feel very tired, Ibu, from driving a long way and I have too many thoughts."

"Don't think too much, Missis, too many thoughts can make your head dizzy," she answers, unscrewing a glass-bottled brew of *beras kencur* as she would have done a thousand times before. "This one is good for your problems, Missis. You will feel fresh again soon." I take small sips feeling the sweet, liquid herbs fill my pores.

"Can I have another one please, Ibu, for a small girl who has recently lost her mother, and hasn't spoken much since; and do you have a special one to give energy to a driver?" I ask, handing back my empty medicine-sized glass.

"Ya Missis, *kukubima* rich in ginseng, or *pasak bumi* will give vitality to a tired man," she says, without a hint of shyness, as she suggests herbal remedies that enhance the sexual function of men. Her knowledge is imparted in a practical way, as if she is telling me how to inflate a tyre. She tempts me to try the *sari rapet* for returning a woman's tightness after childbirth. I take a mental note instead, and let her wisdom continue. "For the child who is sad give *beras kencur*, the same delicious drink you have just finished."

"*Mathur Nuwun, Ibu,*" I nod, thanking her in Javanese as I fold a rupiah note into her palm. I notice her fingers are stained yellow from the turmeric roots in her healing herbs.

"I feel much better now, Ibu."

I can see Pak Sungkar and Yana sitting on the opposite side of the road chatting with a group of neighbours. A small boy is stroking Yana's cat.

"Thank you for waiting so patiently, Pak Sungkar," I sing out as I cross back to the car.

"No problem at all, Miss Lara, we have enjoyed a small rest," he smiles, with tired, bloodshot eyes.

"I'm happy to hear that," I say, and pass him a small glass of cinnamon coloured liquid. "Here is some kukubima, Pak Sungkar. The jamu seller recommended it for you. I see Yana and her cat have made a new friend."

The neighbours greet me politely as I sit beside them on a rickety bench seat made of old planks.

"Where are you from, Missis," a young woman asks.

"I'm from Australia," I smile, "but I lived in Pak Suyono's house over there, when I was young."

Two other women in their house dresses exchange cheeky glances and call out, "*Awet muda*, Missis" you are still beautiful for your age.

"Mathur Nuwun," I say, thanking them in Javanese as I bow my head.

Turning to Yana with a small glass glinting in the sun I smile. "Here is a magic potion. It will make you tall and strong."

"Thank you, Miss Lara," replies Yana sweetly, pursing her lips to test a sip.

"Yana, there used to be a susu warung around the corner from here. The two girls who owned it were sisters. They used to wear the same style of pretty jilbab as you."

I tell Yana about the warm milk drinks they made with honey and cocoa and the *roti bakar* toast they sold at night; and how they even stocked salty-black *Vegemite* spread for Australians like me. And I tell her about the fiery little chili peppers they showed me how to bite with cubes of fried tofu.

"Are you brave enough to eat small hot chilies, Yana?"

"*Belum,*" she says, shaking her head as she strokes her cat—and she means 'not yet'.

As I reminisce about the sisters it dawns on me, they will by now be in their mid-forties like me. Their youth surely fading like mine and the jilbabs that stood them out as different—for being the only two we ever saw in Solo—now blending in with a sea of similar ones.

Fashions had changed in the past two decades. The flared jeans and tie-dyed T-shirts had disappeared from sight. It seemed the generation of longhaired boys in their bellbottom jeans and mirrored sunglasses, who used to burn along Jalan Selamat Riyadi on their 120cc motorbikes—and sometimes sidle past too close and call me sexy—had ridden their carefree, helmetless heads off into the sun and ended the seventies.

"*Ayo*," let's go, says Pak Sungkar, crushing his clove cigarette butt with his leather sandaled foot.

"Yes, Pak Sungkar, Harto has just sent a message to say the owner of the house, Pak Yuda, can meet us in Bausasran at around 5 p.m. He says Pak Yuda hopes we will arrive before sundown when he must go to the mosque for Maghrib prayers."

"We still have plenty of time, Miss Lara," says Pak Sungkar checking his wristwatch. It will take just one hour from here to Yogyakarta.

"I'm pleased to hear that, Pak. We still have time to buy *oleh-oleh* gifts for our families in Yogyakarta."

We pick ourselves up from the curb and brush our clothes down. Yana tucks her cat back into its cage in the boot. It yawns and lets out a lazy 'meow'. The neighbours wave the little boy's hand goodbye, da–da–da–da, they help him say and then to us,

"*Selamat jalan sampai tujuan*" safe travelling to your destination.

"*Terima kasih.* Thank you," we all say in chorus, and to the little boy, "*da-da, da-da–da-da, da-da.*"

Pak Sungkar bumps the Kijang back on to the road and we turn the corner into a street that I must have walked up and down a hundred times in the past. On the left side there is a row of street-side warungs and small restaurants. Each one has a colourful banner advertising its speciality: *Nasi Liwet, Nasi Uduk, Opor Ayam, Rendang, Gule Kambing, Sate Kambing, Sate Ayam, Gurami, Ikan Lele*. A list of spicy curries containing beef or goat or chicken; chicken satay and fish dishes fried or cooked in coconut milk and all laced with green and red chili. There are tempeh and tahu dishes, either fried or boiled, and all kinds of vegetables.

"I will buy *nasi liwet* to take to Tante Sarmini and the family Miss Lara," says Pak Sungkar looking for a place to stop.

"Ah yes, Pak Sungkar. They will appreciate it."

An orange-vested parking attendant waves us over to an empty spot. His wave is almost the opposite of the 'come-over-here' wave we use in the West. He uses his polite right hand, keeping four fingers down and his thumb out. Then he shouts instructions as he guides Pak Sungkar into a perfect parallel park. For this he is slipped a one thousand rupiah note with a slight of hand so discreet that only the trained eye could see it. There is no eye contact between the *parkir* man and his customers. His eyes are firmly focused on directing traffic.

The sun is gradually moving past 2 o'clock but the day is still steaming hot. As we open the car doors again the humid air descends in a blanket of cooking smells. The overriding aroma, a pulverized blend of garlic, onion and spicy chilli, catches our throats.

There are plenty of customers milling around. A small boy in shorts catches sight of me and tugs at his mother's long skirt. She glances over and smiles. His eyes widen with curiosity. A father lifts his toddler to see the colourful foods and drinks on offer behind a glass case on the counter. A black and grey bob-tailed cat winds its way around the legs of a table waiting for scraps. There are customers selecting dishes from the menus displayed on boards. I spy a tempting selection of beans and other vegetables mixed with sliced garlic and green chili. Anything that can't be boiled is being fried in giant woks brim-filled with smoking, precariously bubbling palm oil.

I remember how often Marion and I ate at the small restaurants around here. Gado-gado salad was our favourite dish and we never tired of the savoury peanut sauce—though Marion would always put her boiled egg onto my plate. She had been a vegan by choice since she was a child. I had been an egg-eating vegetarian for two years. influenced by Angus and his conversion away from eating animal flesh.

"Do you know there's more crime around the abattoirs in Chicago than around the whole state of Illinois," he spilled forth one day from his wealth of knowledge. "The killing, and the cattle's fear of it, creates a negative vibration."

His passion and his powers of persuasion were hard to resist, though it was easy to follow a meatless diet in Indonesia where the humble soya bean and a few million eggs can satisfy the protein needs of a nation—until my consumption of eggs became a dilemma.

My eyes were opened to the private life of poultry one day when I was eating alone in a street-side restaurant. A brown-feathered hen strutted out from under a table with her speckled shell presenting. She clucked and clucked around the restaurant and then out onto the road as if searching for help. Never before had I seen how a hen suffers. Her difficult labour was still underway when I paid and left. Later I found out that she was egg-bound. The egg was stuck!

The other diners had been completely nonchalant, continuing to eat silently with their heads down, seeming to relegate the life cycle of eggs and chickens to the farmyard at the back of their minds. Their attention was solely on the food in front of them.

In general, Indonesians prefer uninterrupted mealtimes. Children are taught to focus on digestion. I found a freedom in not having to artfully time a conversation in between chewing and swallowing. As if given a license to fully enjoy the flavours in food. On this chance visit to Solo I was determined to focus my full and undivided attention on one particular snack I had missed—*Serabi!*

15

Serabi is a type of pancake that I could not resist during the months that I lived at the guesthouse, no matter how much will power I summoned. Since childhood I have had an incurable sweet tooth. Solo, with its population of sweet food lovers allowed me to indulge my love affair with sugar.

Serabi are a mix of fine rice flour, white sugar and fresh coconut milk fried in clear coconut oil. They sizzle away to a crispy golden colour in cast iron moulds while you watch. The middle part bubbles into a soft white pudding top. The serabi in Solo are topped with sliced banana or chocolate dollar sprinkles.

The best time to buy them is in the late afternoon when all the shopkeepers along the main street emerge from their midday rest. When trading doors are slid open for the evening and food sellers set up their stalls and carts on the pavements.

"Pak Sungkar, have you tried the serabi in Solo yet?" I enquire, as we dawdle back to the car and he places a tower of boxes filled with aromatic rice dishes and other delights on the front passenger seat.

"Not yet, Miss Lara, but I hear the serabi from Solo are the best."

"Can we walk from here, Pak Sungkar? The serabi sellers are just around the corner."

"The sun is still too hot for Indonesian people, I will easily find another place to park," he chuckles.

My request bemused Pak Sungkar because Indonesians rarely walk in the steamy heat of the day. Walking in the midday sun is for Westerners or Indonesians who don't have a means of transport. Or for a certain nostalgic woman retracing her youthful steps in Solo.

--oOo--

Suddenly I'm twenty-three again. I'm strolling down Jalan Diponegoro on the way to Jalan Selamat Riyadi to buy serabi. I'm alone, as I often found myself after Marion returned to America. My hair is long and dark and shaved in two small spots at the temples. They have been shaved smooth for applying the *paes* paint into black *cengkorongan* curves that represent the Hindi Trinity, Trimurti; a part of the elaborate ceremonial wedding headdress designed to raise the status of the bride to one more commanding of her husband's devotion. The two bare triangle patches left behind, after the paint and heavy makeup has been removed, tell the story of a woman who has just been married in Java.

The serabi seller sees me approach and calls out my order. "*Tujuh, seperti biasanya ya, Miss?*" Seven as usual, Miss?

"*Ya lbu, terima kasih,*" I confirm, with a polite nod.

She notices the tell-tale signs of my recent wedding and wishes me well.

"Selamat, Missis, I see you are recently married," she smiles, handing over a banana-leaf parcel filled with seven warm serabi. She turns to the other sellers along the street and shouts out the happy news. They call out their congratulations with beaming smiles painted all over their faces. They say they hope I will have children very soon. It is the customary wish for newlywed women in Java. But I feel so naive and unprepared and, as I wander along the street back to the guesthouse behind the green gates, it dawns on me that motherhood will be next.

The fertility rite of *ngidak endhog* at a Javanese wedding requires the groom to step on a raw egg until the shell breaks in the hope it will hasten the blessing of a child for the couple. The bride then bathes his foot with flower-petal scented water as a sign of devotion. The ritual seemed to work its mysterious magic for us very well. A week after we returned to Brisbane a few short months later I noticed, while showering with Angus one morning, my breasts had begun to swell.

Our perfect baby boy, Amar, was born a year and a month after our wedding in Solo—an Aquarian child, born at the dawning of the Age of Aquarius.

The fertility Gods had shone a miracle from the realms beyond and caused a celebration on planet earth that day, marked by a flourish of orange and yellow marigolds that bloomed overnight all through the gardens of the Boothville maternity hospital in Brisbane. A floral carpet of blooms led us home through the suburbs to a smaller garden beside a makeshift clothesline, one that would soon work with the summer breezes to flap-dry the added washing baskets full of bleached white cotton nappies hung out like strings of Buddhist prayer flags.

However, I must give the serabi some credit too. Those deliciously guilty calories helped me to gain enough body weight for my monthly periods to begin again after a yearlong hiatus.

16

"Look Miss Lara, luck is with us again. Here is a space to park," says Pak Sungkar, reversing the Kijang to instruction calls from a parking attendant. We park at an angle in between motorbikes protected from the blistering sun with flattened cardboard cartons. Beside them is a row of pedicabs housing drowsy drivers under perambulator covers.

"Come with me Yana, let's look for serabi," I smile, helping to unstick her from the sweaty vinyl seat. The smell of caramel sugar hangs invitingly in the air. "Shall we buy some for Tante Sarmini and your cousins?"

"Okay, Miss Lara."

"Let's order seven, for good luck," I say.

"Why is seven a lucky number, Miss?" asks Yana curiously.

"Because, there are seven days in a week for one thing."

"Oh ya, Miss Lara, and seven colours in a rainbow."

"You're so clever Yana, and you know all the colours."

"I know the rainbow song from the movie *Laskar Pelangi*, Miss Lara. I sang it often with Mama."

"Then we can sing a special version for Mama," I say squeezing her hand. "I will teach you the way to breathe so you can reach a high note. When I lived here in Solo before, I had a friend called Marion who taught me to sing."

Marion had stayed for the wedding but left soon after and I missed her terribly. At first, I arranged my weeks around meditation sessions and cooking lessons and later, teaching English. Angus had been teaching English for all of the time we were in Solo, earning the grand sum of three thousand rupiah a lesson.

Three thousand rupiah would only pay for a parking spot these days or pay to use a public toilet three times in a row—if you should be in such a position—which can happen to travellers who drink iced juice or use tap water for brushing teeth. This was long before the financial crash of 1997, when the world news reported how the rupiah had plummeted and the price of rice skyrocketed overnight.

Harto had been lucky. He was mostly paid in American dollars when the markets crashed and that is how he bought Saraswati all the gold jewellery on her wrists and fingers—and how later she was able to sell it to buy the bricks and steel needed to build a better house. But that is another story. I am getting ahead of myself.

In 1981, three thousand rupiah was equivalent to six Australian dollars—enough to buy groceries for a week, or two train tickets to Jakarta if you saved for a while. That is what we were doing in the weeks before our visas were due to expire.

Native English speakers didn't need a qualification to teach English in those days, far different from now. Having *Londo* skin was considered enough. Londo comes from the word *Belanda*, the Indonesian word for Holland. But it's used more generally to describe any Westerner with pale white skin, no matter which Caucasian persuasion they may be. But without the skills to teach you need self-confidence, or at least some false bravado to stand in front of a classroom of expectant students. It took a while for me to pluck up that courage.

"Don't lean on me," I can still hear Angus say. "Our relationship should be equal. You will just have to steel yourself and do it. We need train tickets to Jakarta."

I can still picture him standing in the doorway of the guesthouse that day, his face pale as though suddenly struck with a fear of having anyone depend on him. Some images stay imprinted forever, as do strong words.

I understood it was fair to pay for one's own way in the world. My father's post-war fear of poverty had seen me working at a local bank the moment I finished school. Still, as far as teaching English, something I wasn't trained to do, I felt like a fish out of water.

Turning to more familiar territory I decided to have some new batik dresses made up at the tailor. If I had to teach, I thought, a professional look might help. Perhaps that is when the seeds of a future in fashion design began to shoot. And I had been given a nudge in the direction my dharma should take.

--oOo--

Before the wedding Angus and I had visited Pak Darno, the paranormal in Kampung Sewu, to seek advice as Pak Suyono had suggested. On that afternoon, after a long pedicab ride from Solo, we found ourselves sipping tea in the cool shade of his verandah peering out across a swathe of rice paddy fields in front of his village home. I can still see Pak Darno in my mind's eye scuffing along the slate tiles to meet us in his black cowhide slippers with his smile and his polite bows.

Pak Darno was a slight man with a gentle character and kind eyes. He dressed in traditional clothes; a brown and gold batik sarong; a woven *rompi* vest, and on his head a traditional *blangkon*, a turban like hat made from batik fabric–a most wonderful look on a Javanese man. This clothing ties the royal subjects of Solo and Yogyakarta to their Sultans and their aristocratic roots, whether a humble *becak* driver or a bupati regent.

Angus and I sat on either side of this spiritual elder in low rattan chairs chatting for a while before he fell in to deep contemplation.

After this expectant silence he imparted that my dharma was best suited to working with my hands.

"Angus, can you tell Pak Darno my mother is a dressmaker. Maybe I should follow her lead?"

Pak Darno smiled and nodded his approval saying it would be a compatible choice; then he closed his eyes again folding his hands onto the pleated sarong that covered his lap.

"You are suited to teaching meditation," he told Angus. "And you must take care of this woman, who will soon become your wife. Your most difficult lesson is to learn to care for others."

I struggled to understand Pak Darno that day though I listened intently. He spoke in a stream of words I recognised but couldn't yet piece together. Angus, who had become fluent in Indonesian during the six months we were apart, was translating both Pak Darno's words and mine.

So blinded was I with adoration for Angus that I thought my speaking Indonesian would impinge upon his territory. And I felt that by deferring to his opinion on every matter I would be worthy of his attention. Thus, a pattern of subservience was established, which continued through the next two decades.

17

When my sisters and I grew into teenagers, my mother asked each of us what we wanted to be. She said I announced in certain terms that I would be married, as if marriage was a career choice. I had just read the classic novel 'Little Women' and apparently misread the feminist message. I had seen myself as the older sister Meg with her traditional values instead of the independent feisty heroine of the story Jo, the character modelled on the author Louisa May Alcott herself.

I dreamed of a warm hearth to share with a handsome man who adored me and I dreamed of baking perfect jam-centred cakes for him to enjoy. If only I knew then what I know now; of the need for a woman to be self-reliant; to stand on her own sure feet and sell those cream cakes to make money instead! But the time has passed. Mistakes were made. There is no going back to where I could have changed track. And besides I was recalling the amount I was set to earn for each English lesson I taught during those last few weeks in Solo—the generous sum of three thousand rupiah, then equivalent to six Australian dollars.

I remember—though would rather forget—the first of those lessons. I recall the classroom full of teenage boys and girls with heads of lustrous, dark hair and doe-brown eyes sitting at their scratched wooden desks.

I can still see the row of open windows along the side of the school building, but I know when walked into the classroom in my new batik dress the air was as stuffy as a closet. As I placed my books self-consciously on the teacher's desk and looked up, the students came to a collective hush.

"It's very hot in here," I said, in English to break the ice.

No response. Just doe-eyes watching.

Feeling awkward and hotter by the minute, I glanced around the room and noticed a pedestal fan with metal propellers in the corner beside the blackboard. A moment later I wished I hadn't. Electricity isn't earthed in Indonesia. The wires must have been faulty. As soon as I plugged the cord into the socket a shock gripped my fingers sending a strong volt through my whole body. I screamed! No reaction from the students at all.

So, there I was, electrified and with no escape and no idea of the teaching techniques I know now. No idea of icebreakers or warmers or hot afternoon wake-up activities, or working together in pairs or groups. All the things I have learned since.

"Please open your textbooks and let's read this page together," I said, summoning my courage through a quivering voice as I held my copy above a heart still thumping from the misdirected current.

Obediently they opened their books and began to read in chorus. Somehow, we filled the hour. Afterwards, at the front desk I signed and collected an envelope containing the three 1000-rupiah notes. I had earned my keep.

"Your husband Angus is a popular teacher," Miss Lara. "He entertains the students with many jokes," the receptionist tells me in English.

"I will let him know later, he will be happy to hear it," I say, slipping the envelope into my purse and bowing out in a hurry.

Escape eventually came in the form of a mini-bus appearing on one of its endless runs up and down Jalan Selamat Riyadi. As I stepped on, I heard the young boys in the back seat say Londo, and giggle behind their hands. It was the second time I had overheard the term Londo used in reference to me. My face flushed all the way to my stop on the same street corner where I had first heard it directed at me.

On that day I had been buying vegetables—cabbage, carrots, beans, small potatoes and some fresh grated coconut—from a roadside market for a cooking lesson at Ibu Mahardi's house. Ibu Mahardi and her husband would later stand in as my parents on the wedding day.

To suddenly recall them reminds me of how Angus and I sat on their laps as part of the wedding ceremony and they said, "The bride and groom are of equal weight." I have photos that display their satisfied smiles, their job accomplished. But the photos don't show the way Ibu Mahardi clicked her tongue while she taught me to cook. Tut-tut-tutted if I added too much of this or that. And tut-tutted in disapproval of my living out of wedlock with Angus.

"That is not the right way in Java, Miss Lara. People will gossip behind your back."

She didn't know that my parents were not happy either—that they didn't agree with my plan to marry outside the Catholic Church, or that my mother had firmly declined an invitation to attend. The path to approval can be heavily scattered with the belief systems of others and for the sake of peace, whether planetary or personal, these must be carefully skirted around. Avoiding labels is an equal challenge.

The day I first heard the term Londo, it came from the mouths of a small group of high school students. The word seemed to cut through the morning air as they giggled past me on their way to school. They were describing me. To be seen as a curiosity in the eyes of others is an awkward feeling, but a good lesson. A reminder to be sensitive towards others, in this case concerning something in which we have no say at all—the colour of our skin.

Though I have my birth country's forebears to apologise for, I suddenly felt the inherited guilt a Dutch descendent might feel, a white-complexioned girl whose colonial forefathers had stolen the reins of the so-called East Indies for three hundred and fifty long years, had wielded power and dominated its people; had plundered its spices, so that all the way to Ibu Mahardi's house I carried the baggage of my whiteness as heavily as the bag of vegetables. I felt the weight despite proudly wearing a new batik dress and feeling a borrowed sense of pride.

18

We received many batik gifts on our wedding day; amongst them a set of bed sheets, a large tablecloth with matching napkins, and some lengths of fabric, most given to us by a wealthy Chinese family. Hired as their private English teacher, Angus had become close to them during the months we were apart—and especially embraced by the loud, brash, generous and soft-bellied matriarch of the family.

An image of her springs to mind. She's scuffing through an expansive marble tiled living room in a red daster dress, pulling rollers from her frizzy hair. There are white capsicum strips stuck all over her legs to ease her rheumatic aches. White powder is patted over her pockmarked face. A slash of red lipstick matches her clown-like character. Her cackling, contagious laugh echoes through the house along with her thumbs-up English, limited to the words 'very handsome' and 'very good'.

There was only one person in the family who spoke English fluently; an elegant woman, who oozed sensuality in the style of the French actress, Catherine Deneuve. Well, that is how Angus would describe her after pedalling his bicycle back from their English conversation lessons.

Still, I had to agree that Ibu Tjoe had a seductive allure. Apart from the ease in which she carried herself, it was in her voice—rich and full. As though she spent her leisure hours swallowing whole plums that stayed comfortably lodged in her throat. Often the memory of a voice can herald an image of the owner's face.

Ibu Tjoe would have been in her late thirties at the time—the age when a woman becomes more at ease with her body. Ibu Tjoe's body was small and her skin lily-white. A soft padding around her hips indicated that she was the mother of the lanky teenage boy who tended to hover around her.

"The boy clings to his mother because his father is rarely at home," Angus explained. "He's tied up constantly with the family's business dealings. I feel so much for Ibu Tjoe."

How I wished Angus would pay as much attention to me, and wondered why, if he admired her curves so much, I was pressured to be rake-thin. Still, I told myself he had my best interests in mind. I hung off every word he spoke and wished so hard that I was the only star in his sky.

Angus said that Ibu Tjoe had connections with the famous Danar Hadi batik stores and that the extended family owned a big car dealership on the outskirts of Solo. Her comfortable car and large collection of batik dresses confirmed his story. She wore simple designs that flattered her neat figure. Her glossy dark hair was styled into an elegant bob with a fringe that brushed the top of her pencil-lined eyebrows. With her full lips bare, she exuded an effortless look of Chinese chic.

"I like your style, Ibu Tjoe," I complimented her one day, as we sipped iced lemon tea in the spacious kitchen of her home. "I never see batik dresses like yours where I shop," I said—which on my budget was usually at Pasar Klewar market.

"Come to meet my tailor," she offered, with her round plum voice. No doubt Ibu Tjoe sensed my insecurity—saw a young woman struggling in the shadow of a husband with charms of his own. In any case she was certainly kind to me. As promised, she took me to her tailor, who turned the wedding gift fabrics into modest dresses for me to wear to school.

Solo taught me a lot about modesty, politeness and Javanese manners that I hadn't known about at first. I learned about polite sleeve lengths, and that rubber flip-flop sandals were reserved for wet bathrooms to guard against germs and slipping. I learned how to sip tea in a social setting, and the way to stoop slightly whenever you passed in front of someone, including in the street.

The royal sister cities of Yogyakarta and Solo command a sophisticated society that I was slowly discovering.

"Passing through Solo brings back so many memories, Pak Sungkar," I say, shrinking with embarrassment to see another flash of myself from the past, as we pull up at a set of lights on Jalan Selamat Riyadi.

There I am at twenty-one again, attempting to cross the busy street. I'm wearing a summer shift and sporting a golden tan. I remember buying the dress at a market in Bali a few days before arriving in Java. Angus had used the travel guide to bargain for a morning price. The dress was a pastel mint green with a scalloped-lace border and shoestring shoulder straps. I thought I looked fresh and summery.

No small wonder the boys who passed by on their motorbikes got the wrong impression, especially if they watched the Hollywood movies that screened at Sri Widari cinema. Those movies depicted all Western women as easy. If only they had known that despite the skimpy summer dress and sexual freedom of my generation, I was in fact rather prudish, and that on first arriving by way of Bali, hadn't realised the dresses I wore during my first days in Java were so inappropriate. After all the unexpected attention it wasn't long before I adapted to sleeves.

But I notice I am alone again on the street as the boys on motorbikes cruise by. Not that I think couples should be stuck together like glue, but I think it's better when there's an equal pull towards spending time together.

Angus had different ideas. His philosophy emphasised individual interests and independence. In his mind he was creating a feminist. But instead, his constant pushing me away resulted in me depending on his approval. I was in awe of his inborn confidence and his rebellious streak that defied established rules. He was the opposite of me and I was drawn to him like a moth to a flame. And it didn't help that in those days I thought him devastatingly handsome, like James Taylor on the album cover of *Sweet Baby James*. Perhaps a trick of the mind caused me to blend the two, which can sometimes be a consequence for those who suffer from a romantic bent. Whatever the case, I was as hooked as a Hindu devotee.

"If we marry it will be in Java," he said. Those were his terms. Like many young people of our generation, he didn't believe in the institution of marriage, as much as he didn't believe in religion. I had no such strong views. All I knew was that I believed in him.

19

The right ingredients for a marriage or anything else are important from the start, I think to myself, coming back to the present and checking that Yana and the cat are both in place.

The right ingredients can make for a successful marriage or a successful snack, like the combination of ingredients that make up sweet serabi pancakes, a significant number of which have just been added to the stack of delicacies on the front passenger seat of Pak Sungkar's Kijang.

"Pak Sungkar, do you mind if we stop by the main street to buy *wingko* coconut cakes?" I ask, wanting to make the most of the opportunity to stock up on more local snacks.

"Yes, of course, Miss Lara, and perhaps we can look for some *ampian* peanut snacks too," he suggests, smacking his lips in a fun and fatherly gesture towards Yana.

"Yes Pak, that is a good idea. Those sweet snacks are on my list of favourites too and I know where to buy them—if the store is still in the same place as it was twenty years ago," noting as I look around a big KFC restaurant that wasn't there before.

"Harto mentioned there is a modern supermarket on the corner across from the vegetable market where I used to shop, Pak Sungkar, and some modern movie theatres too."

"Soon it will be like Surabaya, Miss."

"Yes, Pak Sungkar, there is no stopping that future."

--oOo—

"There is still one person I would like to see here in Solo, Pak Sungkar—a kind woman who attended my wedding. Her name is Ibu Tati."

"We have just enough time, Miss Lara. Do you remember the location?"

"Her restaurant is around the corner from here, Pak. Perhaps she won't mind if we use her bathroom to freshen up."

"Let's go there now, Miss Lara, we can take a rest for a little while," says Pak Sungkar, pulling away from the curb into the traffic heading west on the main street.

"Ibu Tati used to make delicious banana pancakes, Pak Sungkar. They were popular with the foreigners who followed the meditation in those days."

"There are not so many foreigners since the big earthquake in Yogyakarta, Miss Lara. The tourists are not yet brave enough to travel to Java."

"That's true for now, Pak Sungkar, but Java's magnetic power will pull them back."

"Yes, Miss Lara, it is better to be optimistic," he answers, but he says *optimis*—an equivalent word borrowed from English like a thousand others and reshaped to roll more easily off the tongue.

"Pak Sungkar, I hope business is going well for Ibu Tati."

"Don't worry Miss Lara, even if she sells *Indomie* noodles with a few spinach leaves and a poached egg on top, she will survive. There are many mouths to feed," says Pak Sungkar, indicating with a nod the streets alive with people.

"True, Pak Sungkar, and Ibu Tati has her family to help as well. Her daughter was a flower girl at my wedding." And turning to Yana I add, "Her eyes were as big as plates."

"Wah! As big as plates, Miss Lara?" she answers, her own eyes as big as saucers.

"They grew big because she was afraid and because she was wearing sparkly eye shadow."

"Why was she afraid, Miss Lara?"

"Because she was given a special job. She had to wave a feathery white fan to cool my sweating face, while I waited for the groom to appear. I was so happy to have her company but I couldn't tell her because I wasn't allowed to speak or even smile until after the ceremony."

"Why not Miss Lara?" asks Yana, looking befuddled.

"Keeping a serious face is a tradition from a long time ago when couples were matched by their families. The bride didn't know who her husband would be. She didn't know if he was young or old, as handsome as a prince or as ugly as a toad. He might be cruel or kind. He might be rich or poor, tall or short! Too thin! Or too fat! So, you can imagine the bride was scared, and even more scared because she would be sent to live with the husband's family after the wedding."

"How about your husband, Miss Lara, was he handsome?"

"He was very handsome in his wedding clothes. Like a fairytale prince. His black velvet jacket was embroidered with gold flowers to match mine, reminding us we belonged together. And a red and white shawl called a *sindur* was placed over our shoulders as a symbol of courage."

"Do you have photos, Miss Lara?"

"I have a wedding album somewhere. One day I will show you Sari and her big eyes, and me as a bride with my handsome groom."

"Just like Papa in the big wedding photo with Mama, Yana," pipes in Pak Sungkar, having overheard the word handsome.

"Yes, Pak Sungkar, as handsome as you in that photo," I say, winking at Yana, as I recall the ornately framed wedding photo of her parents gracing the peach-coloured walls of their living room in Taman Pinang.

The whole way from Sidoarjo Pak Sungkar has kept the mood light with jokes and singing. I sense no matter how sad he may be feeling he is doing it for his daughter. As we approach Tati's, I notice the Javanese lyrics he sings to the Campursari song on the radio:

> *Kowe lungo neng pasar jarine toko kembang*
> *nanging tekan siiki durung bali...*
>
> You went to the market to buy flowers
> and you never came home...

The lyrics bring back memories of the cactus flowers that bloomed on my wedding night. The *Wijaya Kusuma* blooms just once each year. Before the sun comes up the following day they have wilted. Their spectacular cream-coloured petals look waxy and artificial. They smell both sweet and sour. It occurs to me their scent is a fitting symbol for life, and certainly for my life after marriage, and how, on that night when they bloomed so full in the moonlight, I had misread their omen.

20

"Pak Sungkar, there is Tati's restaurant on the left, the one with the bamboo birdcages."

"Aah—very good, Miss Lara, and there is a parking space in front," he notes, happily bobbing his head as he steers the Kijang neatly in between two similar models that look like matchbox toys.

I tap out a text message to update Harto. He taps back:

Enjoy your time Lara

I'm barely out of the car when I spy Tati at the top of the concrete steps. She's wearing a soft-pink batik daster—her dark hair still cascading in loose waves down to her waist. She catches sight of me and seconds later recognition appears on her face as a radiant smile. She is just as beautiful, barefaced and unadorned, as she was on the night she arrived as a guest at my wedding, with gold-spangled jewels in her hair and her face painted.

"Hello Tati, Wah! I'm so happy to meet again," I call out, as she pulls me up into the familiar space of her restaurant with both hands and pecks my left and right cheeks.

"I'm on the way from Sidoarjo to Yogyakarta, Mbak Tati. These are my neighbours, Pak Sungkar and his daughter Yana."

"*Monggo, monggo*—please, please. Take a seat at this table, Mbak," she offers, calling me sister. "I will bring some jasmine tea. Monggo Pak Sungkar. Monggo Mbak Yana. Please be my guests," she says, offering her right hand to both father and daughter in turn before placing it on her heart in the traditional gesture of friendship.

Her tiny restaurant is set out just as I remember. There are three sturdy teak tables with long bench seats on either side. Each has a few more scratches perhaps, but barely a sign of the years that have passed. Tucked in the far corner is a pedestal fan. Its propeller blades steadily churning the heat in half circles, are edged with grime and street-dust.

"Wah! Mbak Tati, you still have a photo of my wedding on your noticeboard," I gasp, as she fusses at the counter and mumbles instructions to a teenage girl who is busy brushing away the flies buzzing around the food display cabinet.

"I was just telling Pak Sungkar and Yana about my wedding, Mbak Tati."

"Those photos are like souvenirs from the days when Pak Suyono held the meditation sessions, Mbak Lara. I miss the foreigners who came here to eat."

"Your restaurant was our favourite, Mbak Tati."

"There is still a photo album of the wedding on the shelf over there, Mbak. Please, please, show your friends," she says, her face breaking into a smile that crinkles her tiny nose. A few fine lines and a few strands of white hair are the only evidence of the two decades that have slipped by since I saw her last.

"Thank you, Mbak Tati," I say, following her lead in calling me sister, even though as mothers we fall into the category of Ibu, and this is what we are called by others. But between the two of us Mbak brings back the bonds of our youth. And for Yana it is a stepping stool; an elevation to her position.

"I'm touched to see you still have the photos, Mbak Tati. Come Yana, sit here, I will show you Sari and Misti the flower girls," I say, patting the bench seat beside me as I place the faded red felt photo album on the table.

"Pak Sungkar, can I show you my wedding photos?"

"Certainly, Miss Lara, I am curious to see them."

"Look! Here I am bathing my husband's feet. And Yana, here is Sari with her feathery white fan. And see this train of cream flowers in my hair," I show her, running my fingers over the rust-dotted pages. "They had such a strong perfume."

"You look like a princess, Miss Lara," says Yana, her eyes as round as Sari's.

"See here Yana, we are wearing the red sindur shawl. And look, the princely groom is waiting at the entrance doors," I say, flipping over a plastic-coated page.

"He looks so young," remarks Tati, with a nostalgic air.

"Iya, Mbak Tati, twenty years have passed by so fast."

"Those banana palm leaves and fruits decorating the entrance are called *tuwuhan*, Miss Lara," says Pak Sungkar, leaning his head over Yana's to indicate the relevant photo.

"Pak Suyono himself organised all of the decorations and the big brass pots of gladioli. Those men there beside my husband, in their *blangkon* hats, dressed him and placed the *keris* in the long sash wrapped around his waist."

"A keris sword has special powers, Miss Lara. I still keep mine to guard the house from evil spirits," he says, raising his brow as he turns another plastic-coated page. "And like your husband in these photos," he adds, with a mischievous grin. "I was more handsome and slimmer than now."

"Mama told me her wedding kebaya itched," says Yana, snuggling closer to her father.

"Your Mama was right, Yana," I agree. "Being a bride can be uncomfortable. My sarong was wrapped so tightly I could barely walk. I had to be helped up the steps of the pendopo by the *perias pengantin*—the woman who dressed me and painted my face."

"Where is your husband now, Mbak Lara? Still in Sidoarjo?"

"He's working on a project in Jakarta, Mbak Tati. He prefers billiards to running household errands these days."

"*Waduh*! That is sometimes the nature of men," she sighs, while rearranging the condiment bottles on the table with her slim, elegant hands.

"Some men, Mbak Tati, not all, I'm sure your husband is still devoted to you. I remember how he always helped you in the kitchen behind the shell curtain there."

"He is a simple man, but that is true. Without him it would be difficult for me to run this small restaurant."

She signals to the teenage girl fussing with the fly curtain behind the meal counter. "Please bring three bottles of iced tea, Mbak Sekar– and a plate of *rujak* fruit salad."

"That sweet girl is a niece from my husband's village, Mbak Lara. She is learning to cook and to serve customers," Tati tells me, keeping a firm eye on operations and a pause on conversation, before relaxing back into the good points about her husband.

"Ya, Mbak Lara, I have been lucky with my husband. Just now he has gone to refill the gas bottle for cooking."

"Mutual goals and friendship are the keys to a successful marriage, Mbak Tati," I sigh, as she, sensing my sadness, rests a comforting hand on my thigh.

'Monggo, monggo, Pak Sungkar. Monggo, Mbak Yana, please try this *rujak*," she says, switching from a sensitive subject to one more appetising. She spoons spicy peanut sauce in circles over three bowls of freshly cut fruit salad. The delectable contrast of hot, spicy sauce over cool, sweet papaya and melon is a favourite of mine.

"Ya, Mbak Tati, *nanti dulu*," he answers politely, which translates to 'later before' but oddly means in a while, or wait a minute.

"Mbak Tati, we have a cat in the car. Would you mind if Yana nurses it while we talk?"

"Please go ahead Mbak," she urges, calling to her niece to accompany Yana.

"Thank you, Mbak Tati. I say gratefully, as Yana quietly edges her way off the bench seat and whispers shyly, "I will ask Papa to bring my cat."

"Look, he's whistling to the little songbird hanging above the steps, Yana," I say, making a whistle shape of my mouth, because I don't know the word for whistle. But then Mbak Tati says *bernyanyi* which means 'to sing' and I realise that I can get by without the word, for whistle. Though later, in Bausasran, when Harto teaches me a list of onomatopoeic words, I want to sing it as prettily as the songbird at Tati's—*siul-siul, siul-siul*—whistle-whistle.

"That bird is lucky to be in a cage, Yana, so your cat can't eat it for lunch," I tease, but sorry to see a winged creature trapped. Better the double life of Harto's homing pigeons, and mine. Sometimes held securely and sometimes free to fly.

"I like that bird too, Miss Lara, I won't let my cat disturb it," Yana answers, pulling the elastic of her jilbab away from her faintly perspiring neck.

"How about some *ikan lele* for your cat?" calls Tati, thoughtfully suggesting a snack of catfish as Yana patters across the concrete floor in her socked feet towards the sapphire-blue T-shirt stretched over the round tummy of a father who has recently—for good reason—decided to avoid rice.

"Mbak Sekar, please bring some fish scraps from the kitchen," she sings out to her niece. "For a hungry cat!"

"You're very kind, Mbak Tati," I whisper, adding that Yana has recently lost her mother to kidney disease.

"*Aduh! Kasihan,*" says Tati, sucking in a breath. "Such a pity. I will pray that Pak Sungkar finds a new wife in the future, and a kind mother for *si kecil*—his little daughter."

"Any woman who meets him will be blessed, Mbak Tati. He is a kind and gentle man." I say, glancing at Pak Sungkar cradling the fluffy white kitten in one arm—the other arm leading 'si kecil' past our table and down the back steps into the kitchen.

"How is your own daughter, Mbak Tati? Surely too big to be a flower girl now."

"Mbak Sari is married with three children," she tells me proudly. "She lives in Klaten with her husband's family. Close to Prambanan temple."

"Wah! Congratulations, Mbak Tati. That is very happy news, but wasn't Klaten badly hit by the earthquake? How did they fare?"

"*Alhamdulillah*—thanks be to God, they were not hurt but their home was badly damaged, Mbak Lara. The walls are still cracked and even now, a year later, they sometimes relive the trauma. Sari remembers how, in her panic, she rushed to put shoes on the children's feet. Later she noticed that not a single pair matched, either in size or colour. When she finally looked down at her own two feet, one flip-flop sandal was blue and one yellow. She watched the kitchen floor move like a wave while her husband was in the bathroom. Still wet with shampoo in his hair and eyes he managed to wrap himself in a towel and huddle the family to a rice paddy across the road."

"Alhamdulillah," I say, squeezing her arm. "Your son-in-law is a hero, Mbak Tati. I am relieved to hear the family survived. There are so many stories of people who lost loved ones."

My mind drifts to a ragged man I saw one day while walking around a village with Harto. The man was sitting on the rubble of his former home. A neighbour said he had lost his wife and his three children when the earthquake struck. Remembering the scene reminds me to fish a few rupiah notes from my bag. "Let me give you a little help for Sari's family, Mbak Tati."

"When will you move to Yogyakarta, Mbak Lara," asks Tati, tilting her head as she slips the small gift into the frilly front pocket of her pink batik daster.

"Soon, Mbak Tati. I've accepted a job teaching English at a private language school there. It starts at the end of May."

"Will you need a boarding house, Mbak? I have some relatives there with rooms."

"Thank you, Mbak Tati, you are very kind to offer, but everything is organised. I will live with a family I met in Yogyakarta two years ago. They are very kind and reliable. The husband has been managing my affairs since I moved to Indonesia."

But I mention no more than that about Harto. Better for the comfort of all concerned if I tell only my cover story. And it doesn't feel like the right time, and it may never be the right time, because I carry some guilt and torn feelings about it.

"Let me show you a photo of our son Amar, with his green eyes and sandy-blond hair. Not a baby anymore," I say, shifting the conversation to more maternal matters. We lean our motherly heads together over my small digital camera as I show her a few slides of the son I am trying my best not to miss.

"Here is another one of Amar with his fiancé, Alin. Her family is from here Mbak Tati, from Solo."

"Forgive my interruption, Miss Lara, but we must leave for Yogyakarta now," Pak Sungkar reminds, with a glance at the green plastic clock on the wall as he emerges from the kitchen causing the shell curtain to jangle.

On his tail are two talkative heads—one with a headscarf and one without. Two sweet girls already firm friends. The older one is snuggling the fluffy white cat to her cheek.

"Oh ya, Pak Sungkar, you are right. We must go now," I sigh and turn to Tati. "Harto, the man I mentioned, has just sent a message to check our progress. We have an appointment."

"Monggo, Monggo, Mbak. Please, please go ahead."

I had used the word *janji* for appointment, which translates as equally to promise. Whenever I said the word janji, it made me wonder if an Indonesian promise carried as much weight as it does in the West or just the weight of an appointment. But then I already knew how easily a promise of love, professed on bended knee and a wedding vow could be taken back. I'd learned that a promise could be as temporary as the seconds ticking by on the wall clock in Tati's restaurant.

How much better for me then, to rest for a while in Harto's arms and in his quiet presence—to make no promises or demands. To just live and let the minutes tick by into hours, the hours into days and weeks. Watch them tick by and see what the future brings. It seems the cat, settled in Yana's arms again, along with all its secret stories and secret lives, knows this best.

"I'm happy we could meet again, Mbak Tati, I say, rummaging around the depths of my tote bag for an elusive pair of sunglasses, though I hardly need to wear them. The light is less harsh than the light in Australia; more forgiving and gentler, as is my life here.

"Monggo, monggo, Mbak, take care until we meet again."

"Take care too, Mbak Tati," I say as we double peck each other's cheeks like two birds of the same feather.

"We must go now," I sing out to Yana who is standing on the top step peering up at a row of songbirds in cages as decorative as the lace border of her jilbab. She's gripping her cat tightly. One pair of crystal-blue eyes; another of liquid brown are searching for the bird whistling a melody, with its whole swollen chest, into the smoke curls rising from Pak Sungkar's clove cigarette. The shrill key of its sparrow song, pitched far above the sound of the motorbikes whizzing up and down the street, warns the cat.

"Mathur Nawun, Ibu," calls Pak Sungkar, thanking Tati in Javanese as he smiles and tosses his still smouldering cigarette onto the dusty path below.

"*Sami-sami*, Pak Sungkar," she responds with a wave. "And the same to you."

"Are you ready to put your cat back into her cage Yana," I ask as Pak Sungkar opens the boot, and the smell of cat escapes. "Ya, Miss Lara," she responds, by now familiar with the routine.

So there we are, the three of us, back in our respective seats in the white Kijang sedan, accompanied by one satisfied cat. Pak Sungkar has wound down his windows and we are all waving to beautiful Tati standing on the steps in her pink daster dress. Her face, damp with sweat and undabbed parting tears, still wears a smile.

21

As we turn the corner onto Jalan Selamat Riyadi and head west out of Solo, leaving Tati and half a million royal subjects behind, my awareness returns to Pak Sungkar, his daughter Yana and a small white cat. I am also aware that we have one hour to reach Yogyakarta where I will soon see Harto, and that thoughts of him have been constantly with me. Resting as softly as the silk scarf slung around my shoulders.

At the same time, I am totally unaware that another Javanese man—also in his mid-thirties and known fondly as Jokowi—is somewhere in the midst of this Royal City and that one day he will become the governor of Jakarta, and later the beloved and humble president of the Indonesian people.

And I am also unaware that in the happy years to come with Harto, I will form a friendship with an Indonesian teacher. And that she (with her head always in a book) who has read every word ever published by the author Dee Lestari, will introduce me to the lyrical poetry of another man born in Solo, and that I will fall in love with all the words he has penned on the pages we read together in class–the words of the famous writer, Sapardi Djoko Damono, in particular these two lines:

Tuan tuhan bukan?
Tunggu sebentar, saya sedang keluar.

Lord God, are you not?
Hold on a moment, I have just stepped out.

I am unaware of all the wonderous things Yogyakarta holds in store.

"Thank you for stopping in Solo, Pak Sungkar."

"You are very welcome, Miss Lara, he answers, checking both the side and rear-view mirrors. Mbak Tati is indeed kind. I feel fortunate to have met her and seen the wedding photos for myself. For a Western couple to marry in Java is out of the ordinary," he says, picking up speed as he prepares to overtake a struggling truck that is well past its prime.

"Ya, Pak Sungkar, but it's time for me to forget the photos," I sigh, resting back in the seat beside Yana as my thoughts drift into the stream of traffic zipping along in both directions.

"However, the lessons I learned from Pak Suyono and the meditation guides are still useful, Pak Sungkar," I reflect, above the soughing sound of the wheels turning on the tarmac, determined to salvage what I can from those years.

"Best to remember those helpful lessons, Miss Lara. Forget the sad events that cannot be changed."

"Pak Sungkar, there are three lessons I remember well. Strangely one of them involves cats. One of the guides taught us how to release the tension from our bodies into an imagined cat."

"Ah, so cats are multi-talented, Miss," he chuckles. "They can cause traffic chaos and also absorb our stress and worries."

"Haha! Ya Pak, better for us if you keep your attention on the road," I say, getting in on the joke. "How about I teach Yana the way while you drive. Come on Yana."

Yana, though muffling a yawn, agrees with a nod, so I carry on.

"First you need to have a good imagination, Yana. Next you must relax your body, starting with your toes. You can wriggle your toes to make sure you have ten. Then let the relaxed feeling move slowly up your legs and spread into your body. Imagine your body relaxing like a rag doll."

“Like this, Miss?” she says, shuffling a little lower in her seat.

“Exactly Yana. Now relax your chest and shoulders and try to make a space between your shoulders and your earrings?”

“I can feel my earrings,” she says, stretching her neck. As she does, I remember the gold sleepers pierced into the lobes of baby girls in Java, just days after birth.”

“Good Yana, that means you are doing it right. Now, imagine that you have a cat, sitting close behind you. Let your attention drift into that cat?”

“Miss Lara, I don’t need to imagine. I have my cat behind me.”

“Oh Yana, you’ve been doing it all along. But just remember to copy that feeling if you are ever far from your cat.”

“Like a copycat, Miss Lara,” she giggles.

“Yes, like a copycat,” I laugh and pinch her chubby cheek.

“Like the Copycat printing shop,” says Pak Sungkar, chiming in with another joke until we’re all laughing, and letting go of the step-by-step relaxation effort.

“There are two other lessons I learned in Solo, Yana. One involves watching a tennis match. The other involves going to the cinema. But you look like a sleepy cat yourself, so have a nap first. Rest your head on my shoulder.”

“Can you tell me later, Miss Lara?”

“Of course, Yana, don’t worry.”

I text Harto:

We are on the way from Solo Pang.

We have departed Solo but it’s hard to leave the memories of it behind. For a while, my thoughts still linger on the pamong guides of Sumarah.

'Pamong' is a Javanese word meaning to take care of, to educate and to guide. In a village, a pamong is like a teacher, guiding and teaching villagers how to cultivate the land. In the same way, the pamong in Solo guided the meditation students in how to cultivate a peaceful mind. They were not gurus to be worshiped or revered and we were not devotees. They were more like a pocket compass—setting us in the right direction.

There were three main guides: Pak Darno Ong, Pak Wando and Pak Sri. Each man was very different in personality, but each had the uncanny ability to tune in to a meditator's experience. After a special meditation session they would be open to questions, which if asked in English, would be interpreted by Pak Suyono.

If I could use a single character adjective to describe each pamong, I would use 'reserved' for Pak Darno Ong. For Pak Wando with his flexible fingers and animated hand gestures, I would say 'ebullient'. For Pak Sri, with his silver tooth that glinted in the sun when we gathered for meditation sessions on the small porch of his house, I would say 'mischievous'. Pak Sri, by all accounts, was involved with a kind of black magic that rumour said required a follower to spend a pitch-dark night immersed in a shallow stream. The memory eerily invokes the supernatural; a topic about which every student I have ever taught in Java could whisper a story.

Pak Sri was famous for mystical connections, and for the gado-gado salads his wife would make for the meditators, served on a giant lettuce-lined plate with slices of cucumber, tomato and slices of boiled egg arranged in perfect order around the edges. On top was a generous amount of fresh peanut sauce and a scattering of *krupuk* prawn crackers. I suspect that is where my nine-month addiction to gado-gado salad began. After the meditation session she would invite us in off the front porch to sit on woven *tikar* mats in the living room and share it.

"Will we eventually reach Nirvana if we perfect our meditation, Pak Sri," I asked, one bright sunny morning before the salad was served. Pak Sri threw his head back with a chuckle, dashing my naive hopes of spiritual bliss. He answered that our aim was only to live in the world comfortably, with the seen and the unseen, not to escape or to rise above it.

All three pamong had ordinary jobs and lived ordinary lives. As far as I knew, Pak Darno Ong held an administrative job in Solo and rode a bicycle to work. He was my favourite. He emanated calm in the same way as ocean waves lap the shore on a summer day, and it was he who taught the three lessons I remember most.

Pak Dano Ong was a neatly dressed older man with thinning silver-grey hair. He wore prescription glasses with an amethyst tint and a permanent line of concentration etched between his eyebrows. His serious face masked a ready smile that displayed a set of perfectly straight teeth. His voice was a low rumble, as rich as the stories that echoed through the still space of the pendopo from the wise well of his knowledge.

The special meditation sessions were a guide for how to ride the daily ups and downs of life. When I lived with Harto twenty years later, I learned that this way of living was as natural to him as the rising and setting of the sun. He had not been surprised when, soon after we met, I shared what I had learned from the Sumarah guides. His parents had instilled the same attitudes in him: to never disturb others with a loud voice or loud actions; to be humble, to not draw attention. It seemed that like Jokowi, who would one day be president, this way of being was simply being Javanese. The embodiment of all the theory on *rasa* and *kesadaran:* feeling and awareness, I had learned from the Sumarah guides seemed embodied in Harto. The evidence of them and my nostalgia drew me strongly to him and to Saraswati and later to the residents of kampung Surokarsan.

Harto's wife, Saraswati, like her mother and her grandmother before her, was steeped in the Javanese philosophy of acceptance, and of *rasa* and *takdir*: feeling and fate. To be Javanese is to feel as opposed to think, as a Westerner would, about the correct response to life's situations. It is to accept one's fate graciously. Not as in *kalah:* to lose a competition, but rather *ngalah*: to surrender with dignity. As Harto would explain one day, for Javanese people ngalah, or yielding to an opponent to avoid conflict is admirable. Following this is the practice of patience. All things will happen in good time. Next on the list is avoiding harsh or hurtful words. Cutting speech should be sheathed and belted firmly at the back like a Javanese *keris*, a jagged-edged dagger, used only for the righteous defence of self or the protection of others.

And the most powerful of life's lessons—as Saraswati lay on her sickbed during the last of her days—forgiveness. So powerful was her spirit that, as she held my hand in the living room where she lay dying, the ticking clock on the high concrete wall seemed to stop. "I have forgotten everything, Mbak Lara. I have learned that all things, and all times pass. I remember only your kindness."

Oh Saraswati, Saraswati, how I would come to hold you dear, but on the way to see the house in Bausasran that day I barely knew your strengths and fortitude.

I check for text messages from Harto.

Galuh is home now. I will meet you soon.

Yana begins to stir, pressing her head into my arm as she wakes up with a yawn as big as her cat's. I fish around my feet for another plastic cup of Aqua.

"Were you dreaming, Yana?" I ask gently and offer her a sip of water.

"Miss Lara, I dreamed I painted a picture of the sky with some big white clouds. There was a big apple tree with red apples. On the apples were written names."

"Could you see your name, Yana?"

"Not clearly, so I wrote my name on an apple, for Mama."

"Wah! That is a very special dream Yana."

"Ya, Miss Lara, because in the dream Mama was so happy with my gift."

"That is truly amazing! How about drawing a picture of your dream for the memories, Yana, so you never forget? Good memories can become friends."

And so, Yana begins to paint her dream and before my curious eyes, her artist crayon strokes bring its colours into life.

"Yana, I see you are adding a flock of birds to your picture. I like the mix of red and orange and yellow colours you have used for the sky," I say, encouraging her.

"Thank you, Miss Lara but the colour is not correct."

"Aah...that is the sign of a true artist, Yana. If you are satisfied you will never push yourself to do better. But can we leave this one just as it is? The birds and the sky have created a wonderful feeling of freedom and space."

"I will add just a little more yellow to the sun, Miss Lara."

"Aah...yes, you are right, Yana. That is a good idea. More yellow will make the sky seem bigger for the birds as the sun is going down."

After Saraswati passed away, I remember how the sun went down over the Kali Code River in a majestic globe of colour. It was just before Maghrib and for a few moments—as the evening shadows spread across the red tiled rooftops of kampung Surokarsan and the mosques all around sang the dusk prayer into the stillness—I felt the wings of waiting angels there. I wonder if, when Yana's mother left too soon, her little daughter learned of angels too.

"Yana, I have remembered the second story but please enjoy colouring your picture while I tell it," I say, watching her little hands at work. "The story was told by a very wise old man. It goes something like this … Imagine you are watching a tennis match and you want your favourite player to win. You're so excited you cannot relax. The secret is to pay attention to both players equally. Just watch the ball going back and forth across the net. You must be careful not to become the player you want to win. This is also the way to be in every situation. Just observe what is happening as you wait patiently for the result. In the same way if you are riding in a becak on the way to the cinema, and you are running late, you must remember to relax. Don't sit forward trying to embody the becak driver. In this way your breathing will settle and you will feel calm. Arriving a few minutes late will not matter at all."

Relating these stories reminded me of their key lesson: equanimity, and to be aware of the present moment. They reminded me to be patient and enjoy this special time with Pak Sungkar and Yana as we made our way that day to Yogyakarta, and importantly for me, back into the arms of Harto.

Part Two

22

"Pak Sungkar, did you keep the fried chicken's feet from the roadhouse?" Harto has sent a message to say Galuh his sister has returned. "I'd like to give them to her if you don't mind."

"Ya, ya, Miss Lara. Please, please. They are here on the front seat with all the oleh-oleh foods from Solo."

Galuh gave all her daughters chicken's feet to hold as soon as they could grasp. She explained how Javanese mothers believe it will help their children to acquire what they need later in life. Chickens were important in Galuh and Harto's lives. Their mother had raised and sold chickens to get them through school. Whenever we have chicken Harto always picks the bones clean. He especially savours the head.

I noticed he kept his mother's identity card in his wallet the first night we met. I caught a glimpse of her photo across the table and felt a wave of comfort wash over my weary heart. It was evidence of a tender, protective one. A sign that made me trust him from the start. How a man treats his mother, we are taught, is how he will treat other women, and his wife.

He had opened his wallet to retrieve a single *Gji Sam Soe* hand-rolled cigarette, which he lit from a book of hotel matches in the glass ashtray at hand. I was lonely for conversation so I offered him a drink. He refused as expected with a gracious smile. I knew that Javanese manners would have taught him to decline at first, so I insisted until, finally, he settled on a glass of cold beer.

As he smoked, we chatted and he told me about his life, and about his parents, and how his mother was the best one for him, seeming to imply that his father wasn't. Now she was too old to work it was his turn to care for her.

We were sitting in the lobby of the fashionable Yogyakarta Plaza Hotel, where we had organized to meet. He had come to deliver a silk painting, which I had left on hold in a gallery near the colourful tourist precinct of Sosrowijayan that afternoon.

A batik painting to my taste had been difficult to find amongst the loud and garish ones on display, but I was determined to do my bit. The economy had plummeted in Indonesia and tourism had declined since the 2002 terrorist attacks in Bali. Eventually I had settled on an elaborate depiction of birds perched on the tree of life.

Although Harto was dressed in worn Levi's and a faded red checked shirt, everything about him was neat; from his crew cut hair, right down to the dated knife-edge creases in his pale blue jeans and his laced desert boots. His appearance put him out of place with the well-heeled hotel set, which succeeded in arousing a protective streak in me. I was intrigued by his story and encouraged him to tell me more. He was born the youngest of ten children and raised in one of the crowded inner-city kampungs near the Kali Code River that runs down from Mount Merapi in the north.

"I am just small person," he said in English, smiling apologetically for his poor grammar. "People like me just care have enough for eat and enough for live."

But I could see behind those words a sensitive and proud man and, that a hard life had taught him to be resilient and strong. Of course, I would be remiss to suggest it was his story alone that held my attention, and withholding if I did not say that our conversation was mildly flirtatious. Harto was strikingly handsome as well as polite, his posture upright, his body muscular and lean, prompting me to enquire if he had ever studied dance. He shook his head and broke into a smile, saying that far from dance he had only ever trained to be a soldier, but he now worked as a tourist guide. Then he asked if I would like to watch a traditional ballet. Appreciating the offer, I fished out enough money for him to buy two tickets in advance.

From the start I followed an instinct that said I would be safe with this man. I had witnessed a refinement unfold, and a quiet elegance that acted like a soothing balm to my recently shattered senses.

Harto related a story that night; saying that from the age of thirteen his sights were set on joining the air force as a ground soldier. With this dream at the forefront of his mind he had imposed his own strict training regime, planning to apply as soon as he turned eighteen.

Twice a week for six years he ran ten kilometres daily, starting with a few laps of the sports stadium near the family kampung then continuing on to the roads of Yogyakarta. To avoid the heat of the day he would start before sunrise and be home by 6 a.m. to prepare for school. He ran in a pair of navy canvas sandshoes that his mother had bought for him.

He said that as a teenager he would sometimes see soldiers in town. They hailed from the local air force base behind Adisucipto airport. He took note of their muscles, and their proud posture, their starched uniforms and strong leather boots. In them he imagined his future self. He wanted more from life than to follow his father making paper kites and carving garuda statues from copper.

"His money is not enough to feed a family," he said, shaking his head.

He followed his fitness regime until his own ribs were strapped with muscle. To build his biceps he made barbells from steel rods set into buckets of cement, like the ones he saw the older boys in the kampung lifting.

He learned about the air force intakes through a high school friend. The son of a ground soldier based at Adisucipto.

Harto gathered the necessary documents: birth certificate; identity card; a letter of good behaviour from the local police; and letters of recommendation from the kampung officials. He filled in the forms for a selection scheduled two weeks later.

"What time did you arrive on that day, Harto? How many others were there?"

"I left home early in the morning to arrive before seven. There were many just like me already waiting—maybe one thousand or even more. From those only two hundred would be accepted, but I felt optimistic."

"How did you get there, Harto? Did you wear a school uniform," I asked, trying to imagine that day.

"I took the bus in order to keep my energy for the fitness test. My older brother Elang let me wear one of his batik shirts with some everyday trousers. Elang is seven years older than me. He was already married and working as an electrician."

"He sounds very thoughtful, Harto."

"Of all my siblings, Elang is my favourite."

"So how was the test? Did the other boys have muscles too," I asked cheekily, sipping my gin and tonic.

"Not so many looked strong, so I felt confident I would pass," he said, dragging on his cigarette. "Each of us had to show how many sit-ups and push-ups we could do in ten minutes. Then we were ordered to run twice around the track outside in small groups. Some soldiers timed us."

"How about height, Harto? Do you need to be tall for the air force?"

"Not so tall, Lara. The minimum is 165 centimetres. I am a bit taller, but not tall at all compared to Western people," he said with a laugh, as we watched a family of long-limbed Europeans check in at the reception counter.

"For the physical examination we had to strip down. Twelve boys at a time," he continued.

"Were you embarrassed, Harto?"

"Ya, of course Lara, I felt shy, but just fifty-fifty, because the others felt the same. Some were smiling because we saw two of the female soldiers in the office spying our nakedness through the door."

"That's very funny, Harto, but I'm sure they would have dreaded the reverse situation. I know I would."

"Nothing is private in the military, Lara."

"Then I could never join Harto. I value my privacy," I said, not yet knowing that women who joined the Indonesian military were subjected to the indignity of a virginity test.

"Harto said that in the end he didn't need to worry about privacy because his name wasn't on the list of successful candidates. Still, he wasn't ready to give up. He continued to exercise as much as he could. During that time, he finished high school so he increased his runs. At the same time, he joined some neighbours selling batik in Jalan Malioboro. After one year he applied again with renewed optimism. After one week he went back to the air force offices to check the result. Once again, his name was not on the list.

"Afterwards my spirit dropped, and I decided better to forget that dream. The neighbours told me to try the navy, but the problem is I never learned to swim."

"I can imagine how disappointed you felt, Harto," I sympathised.

"Ya Lara, disappointed for sure but my neighbours encouraged me and much later I realised that day was my lucky day."

"Being chosen sounds like a lottery, Harto, so how could it be your lucky day?"

"Maybe I am not sitting here now if I was accepted. Maybe I am already die," he said with a fair grasp of English.

"Ya, that's true," I said, imagining the high risk of dying in the military with all those weapons. But that wasn't the reason.

Harto told me that two years later a military plane departing from Jakarta crashed into a housing complex after the engine caught fire. Only one man on that flight survived. There is a rumour that he decided to take the train that day. The passengers were recently qualified elite soldiers from all over Indonesia. Their bodies were mutilated beyond recognition.

"The air crash disaster happened two days before my twenty-first birthday. I felt relieved and grateful to be alive."

Harto said he felt that fate had favoured him three years before. That fate had other things in mind for him. So, he would work hard at whatever job he could find and trust that fate would not lose sight of him among the many millions.

Later I learned of his deep-seated fear of poverty, born of circumstance. A fear that his future children might suffer the same embarrassment he had felt at having to wear half-mast trousers and ill-fitting shoes. I never told him how I understood that feeling because my childhood did not compare. I'd never gone hungry. But I did tell him that his pride and self-discipline reminded me very much of my father—because, although my father was a lawyer, he had left school at the age of fourteen to support his mother. After he married and then children came along, he studied law part-time for six years while working night and day to pay the bills. There were no extra pennies to spare. He studied to better his future because he had the same poorhouse fears for his family as Harto.

Whatever caused my path to cross Harto's on that mid-March morning in Yogyakarta, no one can say. Whether that intersection was holy ground or just luck, it changed the course of our lives, and filled mine with the kind of riches I would never trade for cash.

Certain things drew me to him: his underlying pride; the slow sophisticated manner in which he crossed his legs; the way his fingers held the glass so elegantly. He had a reserved assuredness about him and a fine-featured angular face—with molasses eyes that lit sparks in me far beyond sympathy. His skin was dark. Too dark to attract a wife, he said, and beamed self-effacingly. Assuring me. He had a regal air about him, and one day Amar would say, "Harto is like a king."

That night I had chosen to wear a fan pleated skirt in black silk chiffon, and a pure silk jersey top to match—on my feet a pair of low Italian heels in soft tan leather. Indulgent purchases pulled from the travel wardrobe I had packed for the six-week trip. Extravagance excused as quite essential after years in the world of fashion. Still, they had more than paid for themselves that night. Harto had noticed the woman in them—the woman he said was still beautiful—the woman beneath the clothes.

23

The following night Harto accompanied me to a performance of the Ramayana Ballet held in the amphitheatre near the Sultan's Palace. He arrived at the hotel dressed in a crisp indigo and white striped shirt; one that he would wear again on special occasions over the years that followed. He smelled faintly of his signature scent, which I would come to know very well and find a comfort.

I still keep a vial in my dresser drawer—all these years later—given as a reminder of love in a parting gift. Trust Harto to be so thoughtful when I had to leave in such a hurry. When we feared that circumstance might see us parted.

"Medicine for your heart," he had whispered, folding the bottle into my hand. Eyes as soft as mink.

The perfume he wore was a street copy of Kenzo, purchased for a fraction of the original's cost, but the fragrance of it could fill a forest. A waft can bring back moments in time; a flash of his face, his silk-skinned body fresh from the shower wearing nothing but a towel—lip-syncing the lyrics to campursari—and spilling me into stitches on the Persian carpet with his elastic dance moves.

Who would have thought that I, who walked into his life with my Chanel No. 5, would willingly sacrifice that finer scent for such laughter and those more necessary things in life? The smell of satay cooked over charcoal for instance; a cob of roasted corn; a glass of ginger tea—of the companionship to share it with and the touch of a hand.

On the night that Harto took me to see the ballet he was dressed for chivalry. The bold-striped shirt he wore was tucked with soldierly precision into firmly fitted black jeans. On his feet he wore a pair of army boots that added to his height. His dated style seemed to slow down time; to make the world of fashion I lived in feel redundant and a career that revolved around selling a new season's wardrobe four times a year fade rapidly.

When reception called to say he had arrived I hurried down the stairs to meet him, still dressed in a sarong and summer shirt.

"You better come and wait in my room," I laughed apologetically. "I need some advice on what to wear."

"Take your time. Don't worry," he said gently. "No need to hurry."

I remember the stillness that descended as he entered the room, and how carefully he closed the door latch so that it barely made a sound. And how perhaps I should not have felt so much at ease—but how I did from the start.

Strewn over the bed was a selection of evening clothes; among them a silk blouse I had bought at the airport terminal in Sydney—and a recently purchased Indonesian kebaya.

"Please help yourself to a cool drink from the bar fridge, Harto," I offered, scooping up the wardrobe choices before disappearing into the bathroom to change—my heart faintly skipping.

"Which blouse is best for the ballet Harto, this one or the other?" I asked, stepping into the bedroom still buttoning the line of hooks on the kebaya.

"All are good," he nodded, observing thoughtfully, from where he sat on a gold velvet guest chair.

Finally, I settled on the kebaya from the famous design house of Prajudi. A garment of transparent ivory silk taffeta, embroidered with delicate black spider lilies. I had recently discovered it in a Jakarta boutique; something I no longer wished to recall because the circumstances around its purchase still hurt—as if the needle that pierced the fabric had missed a stitch and punctured my heart. Best to not think about Jakarta. Best to look forward, not back. Best to embrace the now and the warmth of a Yogyakarta night, and the gentle company in the room with me instead. Best to enjoy the night with Harto and some much-needed respite. To spray some perfume, throw a lipstick, a silk scarf into a purse; to throw caution to the wind and feel the glimmer of happiness again.

I felt Harto's eyes fix on me as we followed a queue of well-dressed tourists into the theatre restaurant. We ate together at a table for two before the dance began. I ate with an uneasy awareness of how expensive and wasteful this must seem. Harto was nonetheless well mannered and polite but when we got to know each other better extravagance like this would be declined.

We skipped the smorgasbord of cakes and desserts that night and made our way into the amphitheatre, choosing bench seats towards the back, away from the main crowd of visitors congregated around the stage. A blanket of warm air settled over the audience, abuzz with curiosity and gasps, as costumed dancers began to appear amongst the crowd, fuelling expectations of what the night might bring—and as we sat just close enough to feel each other's body warmth—what the night might bring for us.

Throughout Java, public displays of intimacy are considered impolite. The royal city of Yogyakarta is not the right place for a Parisian style street embrace. We sat as close as good manners would allow and once or twice, as we watched the performance, Harto gently stroked my back, the warmth of his touch instantly melting my bones into flesh.

—oOo—

A Wayang Orang performance of the Ramayana ballet is a mesmerizing spectacle to behold. The stage springs to life with a cast of good and evil characters in elaborate batik patterned costumes, heavily accessorised with gold filigree headpieces, armbands and gold pointed elfin ears, tinkling bracelets and anklets. And for Rama and Laksmana, his warrior brother, gold tipped arrows and gold decorated bows.

Dancers transform themselves into living puppets before your very eyes, performing arm movements that defy reality. To the side of the stage there will be a gamelan orchestra of cross-legged musicians, timing percussion, gongs and flute sounds to the epic drama's rise and fall, and intermittently the ethereal voice of a *sinden* soprano singer.

"The character you see now is Buto Cakil, Lara. He is my favourite," Harto commented at one point, his eyes fixed on the stage as a male dancer shook his woolly wig of black dreadlocks, tied with a headband over a white plaster demon's mask.

"Karakternya jahat tapi gerakkanya paling sulit," he said, translating the words for good measure into his thickly accented English, "his character is cruel but his movements are the most difficult."

Harto knew the characters and the story very well. I knew only a part of it. My son Amar's name had been inspired by its hero king Rama. Harto had often taken tourists to see the play and learned the story. These background snippets interlaced as we watched the dance and picked up common threads from each other's lives.

We took blue taxicabs that night, holding hands as we drove through the lamp-lit streets—the atmosphere spiked with unspoken expectation. When we arrived back, we stepped tentatively together up the big spiral staircase to my room...to bed…and….and here I shall ask you to bow to the rules of Javanese reticence and reveal no more than that, suffice to suggest the caress of silk hands on bare skin; a swathe of velvet kisses and warm streams of breath; and the slow, slow gentleness of it all. And to feel three years of loneliness lifting, dissolving into the darkness, like ink swirls in an ocean.

Harto left in the morning and I stayed in bed. A cloud of euphoria lingered for hours but I had second thoughts about meeting him again. I worried it might be a mistake to get involved. He was only thirty-four and I was twelve years older and still married, though by the finest of threads. I called my youngest sister in Sydney to confide. My brave-hearted more adventurous sister. The jazz singer-solo-world-traveller-risk-taker sister. The opposite of me! She laughed and said I needed to have some fun for a change. By that time, most of the people in my life thought the same.

As it happened, I would have plenty of time to contemplate the idea of a short affair. For now, I hesitatingly decided against it. Besides, I had a previously arranged sightseeing tour of Java to get through first. Best to be responsible as usual, I thought.

Later that week, Harto arrived to say goodbye and help carry my luggage to the lobby.

"I will miss you very much, Lara," he said, accepting the news with good grace, but I could read the disappointment in his eyes. I can still see it now in my mind's eye as I watch him smile and step slowly down the hotel foyer stairs to leave, knowing we may never meet again. His stalwart acceptance and his humility, and the strength of those two things combined, composed him. I knew well from my time in Java before that these two qualities are highly prized. Harto had conquered them both. In the years I have known him since, this internal compass has been his guide.

24

My guide for the trip I was about to undertake was the opposite—an art student called Santo, who I happened to meet on my flight from Australia.

He had boarded the flight late, due to an excess-baggage problem that delayed take-off. After finally appearing to the collective relief of passengers, he had scrambled over some sleepy ones into the empty seat beside me. He seemed genuine at the time with his profuse apology and wanted to converse.

"I had too many books," he said nervously, smiling after our plane had bumped through the clouds and settled into blue skies.

"What kind of books," I asked, and the conversation continued from there, above the engine drone. We talked about art and his ceramic pot designs and galleries and food and family, his birthplace of Madura and his aspirations for the future. Then switching to a more collusive manner he mentioned the future of his struggling artist friends, and how the kindness and generosity of sponsors would greatly help him to help them.

"It would be his pleasure," he assured, to introduce me to these protégés. And then in a more relaxed manner now the main concern was off his chest, "When will you come to Yogya?"

"I'm not really sure," I responded, looking into the capsule space of the Boeing 747 and wondering myself.

"I can show you Borobudur, Prambanan, sunset at Parangtritis and many more tourist places," he said, shifting upright in his seat. "I have many friends who can help with everything, and a good driver, and anything else you need. Just let me know," he said, leaning closer before complimenting me on the highlights in my hair.

"I have seen those places before," I smiled, returning his, and noting with fascination his elegant hands with their long-manicured nails—and his wide pencil-lined eyes. Or were they? I looked a little closer. No, they were naturally lined at birth.

"Yes sure, why not," I agreed, starved of attention from Angus and seduced by Santo's offer. With such an intriguing character, I thought it might be worth seeing those sights again.

Santo had a talent for flattery, which was easy to see past, but a persistent manner not as easy to deflect. I kept his email address in case, and because I had a vague feeling the meeting might be fate. I was on a flight to reunite with Angus in Jakarta and not expecting it would go well. My feeling was confirmed the moment I caught sight of him at Sukarno Hatta airport terminal.

--oOo--

"Why couldn't you get a taxi? I had to leave a meeting!" he snapped, shrugging off my hesitant attempt at a hug as he retrieved my bag from the carousel and headed for the exit. His world was different now. It was a world away from mine.

Later he took me to a crowded bar full of middle-aged white men playing billiards. Local girls in mini-skirts and stiletto heels hovered here and there.

"I'm captain of a team here now," Angus remarked, clinking the cubes of ice in his glass of scotch and soda as he scanned the room with a smug smile. 'Some of the girls play better than the men."

"Maybe I should try to learn," I answered, feeling out of place and as fragile as the thin stemmed cocktail glass in my hand.

"You've never been interested before. Why would you now?" he retorted, blunting my efforts to create some common ground.

"Did you notice the waitress who served our drinks," he asked.

"Yes, she smiled at me. She looks no more than sixteen," I said. "What a pity she has to work in a bar like this."

"It's not a pity at all," he guffawed. "The expat men here make sure the girls are well looked after. One has just paid the rent on her boarding-house room for the year."

"Oh, I see. You're all very kind," I said. But what I saw was the writing on the wall in large letters. The message that said I was sorely cramping the new lifestyle Angus had found in the capital—one that lay well outside the bed we had shared.

After the emotional shock in Jakarta, I decided to take up Santo's offer of a sightseeing tour around Java, because nothing seemed to matter much. What could I possibly have to lose? Any change of scenery sounded good. I postponed my return ticket to Brisbane and flew directly to Yogyakarta, and a fate I never expected.

--oOo--

On the day allocated for the tour, Santo arrived at the hotel with a flourish three long hours late. He was wearing a fashionable batik shirt and an air of importance. He had been delayed, he said, at a university, where he had been asked to give a guest lecture. Though he had the number of my Nokia phone, he had not updated me with this change of plans. For hours after Harto left I had waited in the lobby of the Plaza Hotel, expecting a better excuse and felt offended.

His behaviour put me on the back foot from the beginning, while his arrogance grew with each leg of the trip. Life was about to hand me a three-week package deal, which included a timely lesson on the need for assertiveness.

For three weeks, Santo pushed me into plans that suited him and fitted better with his troupe of artist friends than me. The more he excluded me from decisions the more I felt caught in the undertow of being taken for a ride. While Santo fast-talked with his fellow students in Javanese, I footed the bills and bided my time, vowing never to get myself into a situation like that again.

Later friends and family said it was obvious from the start. But I had to learn my own lessons. I had to weigh things up without the sounding board that coupledom provides. I was just beginning to negotiate the world as a single woman. It seemed I would need to look at both sides of the coin more carefully.

On the up side, I was learning that one side tends to balance the other. In this case it was Santo's photographer friend who put things into a better light. Not only with his camera but also with his character. He was the flip side of the coin that had tossed up Santo and every part of him was the opposite.

Sarjono, as he introduced himself shyly, was a media-studies graduate from Yogyakarta Institute of the Arts. He completed our intrepid group of four:

Pak Budi, our balding buck-toothed driver, who was somehow able to squeeze past pedicabs parked in alleyways with minimal scratches to the car; to skirt cleverly around any vehicle in our path and to miraculously find places to park whenever he had to pray at the mosque.

Santo, as self-appointed guide, for better or worse, and a former fashion designer in her mid-forties; mother of a twenty-year-old son still at home in Brisbane, and wife to an Australian husband on a posting in Jakarta, highly successful in his career but not so much in marriage.

Sarjono had been seconded by Santo to video-record the trip as we crisscrossed Java, and it seemed as a confidante when it came to all decisions on where to stay. Santo, as trip advisor and translator to Pak Budi, sat in the front of the faded green hire sedan—one that had seen better days. This would enable him to do the best job, he said, nodding away with his travel books and brochures in hand, and the lump sum of cash I had given him to manage affairs, tucked securely into his satchel.

"Sarjono will accompany you in the back seat," he said. And with that we set off bumping along the roads of Java in a full car with very low suspension.

From time to time, Sarjono would tell me stories about his family, and where he came from—say that his father was a policeman, whom he feared a little—a hard man who did not agree with Sarjono's choice of career.

"My personality is the opposite of my father," he chuckled, "but I must respect my parents and show gratitude; that is our culture."

Along the way we stopped in at his home, in the highland city of Batu in the east of Java, to drink tea with this father of stern stature and few words. The house mirrored the neat and polished appearance as its high-ranking officer owner. On the wall of the entrance room, reserved for receiving guests, hung a gold-framed graduation photo of Sarjono. The approval of his youngest son, though unspoken, was on proud display.

In the kitchen I met his mother, Ibu Feni, round and warm and jolly. She was giving instructions to an elderly cook.

"This is Bu Ayushi; she has lived with us for many years," she told me, bursting with pride. "She was Sarjono's nanny and now she has become part of the family. She helped me to raise Sarjono from the time he was born. We are making his favourite snacks to take on your journey tomorrow. Would you like to learn how to make *klepon* coconut sugar sweets, coloured green with pandan leaves, Miss Lara?"

With surprise and delight I replied, "I would like that very much, Bu Feni.

"The sweets will be rolled in shredded coconut."

"May I wash my hands in the basin over there first, Ibu?"

"Go ahead, Miss Lara. Please make yourself at home."

"I have been curious to learn this recipe, Ibu Feni," I said, catching a glance of my pale skin and fading lipstick in the mirror tile above the tap. "I have a sweet tooth."

"Aah… you are just like Javanese people, Miss Lara."

"True, Ibu Feni," I laughed and patted her shoulder as we three women laughed. "Sometimes I feel I was born in the wrong place. Or perhaps it is because I was married in Java when I was young."

But I stopped there and I let her believe that my marriage was as content and stable as hers. Perhaps it was then that the facade of a happy marriage to answer all future queries was born. A fairytale wedding in Java with a generous and kind man would later serve me well as a smokescreen for my relationship with Harto. No further questions would be asked. And I found that a happy story takes less energy and spares the teller from ever facing the facts.

"Your house is lovely, Ibu Feni. I like the aquarium in the living room with the big gurami fish."

"Growing that monstrous creature is a hobby for Sarjono's father," she sighed. "Anything to do with fish is a distraction from the pressures of his job. There is a pond in the garden too, Miss Lara, full of catfish. Later we can take a look."

"Aah...that is a very good idea, Ibu Feni. Watching the way fish move in the water is a nice way to relax."

"Rolling the green pandan sweets is also relaxing, Miss Lara."

"And the warm company of the women in this kitchen, Ibu Feni," I smiled, as three pairs of sticky hands whiled away an equally sticky afternoon at the rice flour covered kitchen table.

"After Ibu Ayushi boils the sweets in water, we will roll them, Miss Lara."

"So that is the secret to the melted palm sugar centres, Bu Feni," I laughed, as if a light had suddenly switched on and made the day brighter.

"Yes Miss Lara. That is the secret," she said peering over her reading glasses.

"What secret is that Ibu," asked Sarjono, appearing in the doorway with a camera in hand.

"Never you mind," said his mother fondly. "Better if you take some photos of us cooking for Miss Lara—for souvenirs. And afterwards take a mandi to freshen up, and change that dark shirt to one more colourful, perhaps the yellow T-shirt Ibu Ayushi ironed yesterday in readiness for your visit," she fussed, in her loving-mother's way.

"This kitchen looks like a klepon factory—someone should test the flavour," he teased gently as he poked around the table for stray pieces of palm sugar.

"Not yet, my dear child. Come back later," she said brushing him off. "For now, you can try one of those *mana lagi* apples that Santo brought from Malang instead."

"So those sweet, yellow apples are actually called 'where again' apples Ibu," I noted with a laugh conversing more easily as my Indonesian gradually improved.

"Ya Miss Lara. The name says that after eating one delicious apple you will look for another one."

"I will take an apple each to father and Santo, but later I will not look for more apples," winked Sarjono to Ibu Ayushi. "I will look for the klepon sweets," he added as he loped away with a face that feigned disappointment over his rejection as a glutinous-rice-flour candy taster.

Unlike the steel figure of his father, Sarjono was small boned like his mother with a slight paunch that relaxed a little over the leather belt of his jeans. He possessed a photographer's arty look, dressing only in black: black bootleg jeans, black T-shirts and black cotton twill shirts with a top pocket for his *Gudang Garam* cigarettes, his sleeves rolled up for comfort. His frizzy *kribo* hair was tamed into a short ponytail, which suited his dark complexion. His clothes acted like a simple canvas behind all the camera equipment he needed to carry. But what I remember most about Sarjono and his mother is the kindness that radiated from their soft brown eyes.

While we walked around the cities of Malang, Semarang, and Surabaya Sarjono told stories he knew of the heritage buildings, always speaking slowly in Indonesian. I would listen intently, smiling, nodding, wanting to learn, grateful for his patience.

Sarjono explained one day that his name meant 'educated', as that is what his parents had hoped for him to be. I can vouch that he was. Where Santo failed in good manners, Sarjono excelled. While one bolted down double serves at dinner and ordered dessert, the other ate little and refused seconds. Sarjono's posture, as he kept me company in the places we visited, would sometimes stoop as if in apology for Santo's arrogant airs. His helpful nature, as we explored, was a comfort and his talent for taking films and photos a gift I would long treasure.

One character so gentle, the other opportunistic, calculating and greedy. One of them more like Harto, who for all this time I had been remembering and missing. I hoped that I could see him again.

As the three weeks progressed it became clear that Santo was no saint, but as devil's advocate he helped me to see the type of company I would prefer to keep. But without him, the life I lived in Java may never have begun. He was the stepping-stone that led me back to Harto.

Still, I was grateful for all that I saw and learned along the way. I had feasted my eyes on stunning harbour views from the top of the lighthouse in Semarang. I had delighted in the discovery of Hotel Candi Baru, in all its antique glory—with its tiled baths brimming with cool water—and the apple orchards in Malang, bursting with fruit. In a small gallery in Surabaya, I discovered exquisite paintings by the artist Mas Dibyo. His works, exuding all the strength and beauty of the feminine, stood out from all the disturbing ones of bloodshed and mass killings, and the many images of cockerels. In one of Mas Dibyo's paintings a mother is dressed in rich maroons and greys with one child tied onto her back while she cradles another. How I regret succumbing to Santo's pressure to direct the money it would have cost into his own art projects instead.

But Santo's behaviour did not diminish the beauty of the mountains, rivers and waterfalls, or the kindness of strangers we met along the way.

Far removed from Santo and his network of art gallery owners, Harto did not have a mobile phone, but thankfully the foresight to give me a note with a landline number on it and a message written in Indonesian.

He wrote it on the hotel notepad in the careful strokes of his signature capital-letter style. I kept it in my wallet for years until one afternoon when a wet season house flood in Bausasran submerged all my belongings and washed the ink into a blur.

"Boleh titip pesan buat Mas Harto," the message said. He helped me to practice the words, repeating them slowly. "Boleh titip pesan. Buat Mas Harto." May I leave a message for Harto?

The landline number belonged to his neighbour fondly known as Ayung Uti—everyone's grandmother. I would find out later she was the kampung treasurer and the only resident to have a telephone.

"If you need me, you can call Ayang Uti," he said in the warm timbre of his deep voice as he handed me the note before my journey with Santo. I folded it carefully into my wallet. Three weeks—and a few hard life lessons later—I called the number from a Jakarta hotel on my way back home to Brisbane. I heard the crackle of a woman's voice over the line as she called for Harto, and then the shuffle of feet and more voices and a few minutes later, the warm sound of his voice. He said he had missed me and asked if I would come back.

"Yes Harto, very soon," I answered, both hands grasping the receiver.

"I love you," he pitched nervously into the phone, as if he had silently rehearsed the words and this was his chance at last to set them free. It was March 2004. I returned in July.

25

I brought gifts from Australia: a small Nokia phone for my sake as much as his; a pinstriped cotton shirt in the classic style that he wore, and a stainless-steel watch to replace the bright gold one he was wearing when we met. My fashion background had got the better of me while I was back home in Brisbane and I had succumbed to shopping again.

"So, you're going to turn Harto into a model," Amar had called out as he dived onto the sofa in his designer jeans, grabbing the remote.

My son, Amar, had been surrounded by fashion since the age of four when I began to study design. From time to time, he had been called upon to model on the catwalk. Now aged twenty he had determined his own style—James Dean denim and fitted white tees. Smack bang in the middle of a carpentry apprenticeship, he was learning how to build houses and building the muscles to match.

"Just keep things simple, Mum," he reminded.

I hoped I would not change Harto, I thought, and called back from the bedroom,

"No, of course not, Amar, they're just practical things, don't worry."

I had lived half my life under the critical eye of his father and would not want to pressure another person to change. The uneasy feeling of being remoulded a bit here, reshaped a bit there, knowing you won't ever reach the mark chips away at confidence. I wanted to be loved for who I was, with all my flaws, and I must remember this in regard to others. Still, I had already purchased the gifts and they were going into my suitcase, for practical purposes, and because I wanted to even up the material side of things a bit.

--oOo--

After a mix-up with hotel bookings and no way of contacting Harto, he had waited for hours in the foyer of the Novatel until I finally arrived in an airport taxi.

"Never mind Lara," he said, a broad smile flashing across skin as beautiful as the night that had by then descended. We continued in the same taxi to the Phoenix Hotel, both so relieved to see each other again that we laughed and joked for the entire ride.

'You repair me," Harto said shyly, as he opened each gift the following morning. He would not have seen the thought that flashed across my mind as I watched him from the tousled bed. That it was he who had begun to repair me. He was trying on the new watch I had brought from Australia. We were spending our first week together—a week that felt at once warm and safe, loving and familiar, and yet surreal, otherworldly and unfamiliar. At home but not my home.

The latest news from Angus held no promise of reuniting, but even with Harto's care and attention, I felt shaken from the life I had known. The following week I enrolled in an intensive Bahasa Indonesian course at a local university. If I was to stay, I would need more fluency in the language.

"Miss Lara, we are approaching Prambanan Temple," Pak Sungkar calls, pulling me from these recollections to the page on which Yana is still happily drawing, and attracting us both to the giant stones that have fallen on the temple grounds.

"The stones fell during the earthquake that damaged Tante Sarmini's house last year. Thankfully the neighbours have repaired the walls," Pak Sungkar placates.

"That's good news, Pak Sungkar. Harto and his neighbours also formed groups to repair the damage to kampung Surokarsan at that time."

"In Javanese this mutual help is called *gotong royang*, Miss Lara."

"Like everyone here, I will never forget the morning of the earthquake. I was visiting relatives in Brisbane when Harto called."

Harto's voice had boomed down the line from his silver Nokia phone against the background noise of people shouting, car horns and traffic. He told me Saraswati had broken her front teeth on the doorframe while she was trying to escape the house. He said that everyone else he knew was fine, apart from an old aunt who had suffered a broken shoulder, and that Taufik, a seven-year-old boy I had played ball with once, would soon be laid to rest. A roof beam had fallen and hit his head. A few houses in the kampung had been damaged but escaped the worst. Harto said he and his neighbours had formed gotong royang groups to fix what they could while they waited their turn for government help. I was so sad to hear of Saraswati's accident. How distressed she must have been. Besides the crowning glory of her hair, she was proud of her straight white teeth.

"She is covering her mouth with a scarf because she feels so shy," Harto confided.

"Can you take her to a dentist soon, Harto? I am more than willing to help."

"Thank you, Lara, she will be grateful."

By the time I saw Saraswati a few weeks later, a denture had been fitted, but for the weeks I stayed she still covered her mouth.

"She still feels the trauma," said Harto, "but she never complains."

The door that Saraswati had stumbled through was the door to their tiny home. The door was low and narrow as was the house, and there were five family members living in it—not to mention many rats. The rats' days were numbered after that, as were those of the house. Harto had internally resolved to knock it down, to take revenge on the house and the rats and build a new home—a better one—rat proof!

It would take another five years for the house of Harto's dreams to materialise for Saraswati. The new house would have high ceilings —with a second floor too high for rats to jump on—and a sewing alcove where Saraswati would put her Singer treadle machine.

Fate would summon a major eruption of Mount Merapi in the meantime, providing copious quantities of volcanic sand that would wash down the Code River. Harto would don his cargo shorts and black galoshes and shovel bucketloads over many weeks storing the black sand in bags against the riverbank wall. This valuable resource would significantly reduce the building costs. Later the sand would be mixed with cement bought from the sale of Saraswati's gold jewellery. Though the wait was long, Harto rarely mentioned these plans, leaving time and his intention and—when opportunities such as these arose—preparation.

Benih yang ditabur akhirnya akan dituai.
Seeds planted in a rice field will eventually yield.

The shaking lasted a full minute on the day the earthquake struck Yogyakarta. Five thousand people, lost their lives, mainly in the south. Saraswati had been relatively lucky. Less than ten years later her luck would run out.

From Harto's account many people from the kampung slept in Alun-Alun, the palace square, that night—fearing aftershocks. A few residents picked up hookworm from sleeping on the ground. Harto was one of them. Neither of us knew a thing about hookworm until then.

After Harto called that day my relatives and I gathered in the living room of their house on the Brisbane River to watch the news reports on the television. To hear the word Yogyakarta in the same sentence as devastating earthquake, deaths and disaster wrenched my heart.

Harto called again a few days later. I booked a flight for the following week. By the time I arrived at Adisucipto Airport, the hookworm had lumped an itchy trail right across his lower back.

"Tidak apa apa, itu masalah kecil, pasti sembuh sendiri," he said stroking my face in bed. "Don't worry, it is just a small matter. It will heal in time."

But I had seen the tracks the hookworm had made in just one week and I wasn't so sure. My older sister had warned me, when I'd called her for advice, that the lifecycle of hookworm larvae in a human host is six weeks. In that time, they can crawl a metre.

"Harto," I persisted, "can we see a doctor in the morning to check?"

"That will cost much money, Lara. It isn't necessary."

"Please Harto. It is more than necessary for my peace of mind."

If only I had known the local treatment would be so shocking, I would never have pushed him to go. The doctor who treated him brushed a type of acid onto his back. The solution burned through seven layers of skin and left a scar for life.

26

In the two years before the earthquake disaster struck, I had made bi-annual trips back and forth from Brisbane to Yogyakarta. By then Amar was close to completing his apprenticeship in carpentry. His plan was to join Angus in Jakarta and look for construction work.

With Angus mostly absent during those two years, I hadn't wanted to leave Amar for long periods. The maternal pull to provide solid ground for him was strong. So, while he filled the house with friends and fun and laughter, I filled their stomachs. I wanted him to have a warm home, healthy meals, clean clothes, fresh sheets and a parent to offer guidance, though I was struggling to find my own.

Angus had been home once or twice during that time, but he wasn't the same person who left. The one who said living without me would be hard; the one who had raced Amar home from the Baskin Robbins ice cream shop one summer afternoon, laughing as he ran up the long driveway with my favourite toffee ice cream dripping down a waffle cone. The one who could detect the sore spots when he massaged my shoulders and neck. The one who had held me tightly and promised to miss me every day he was away—words that now held no weight. Words that fluttered down like the falling leaves that washed into the gutters along with the winter rain. At night he was silent, turning his back to mine in a bed that had once been a warm refuge. The door had been firmly shut on over twenty years of intimacy.

"We should be lovers always," he had said, fearing his demise into domesticity, and I had trusted. I never imagined the freedom to touch could be snatched without warning from beneath your feet; the carpet rolled up; the curtains drawn; the lights flicked permanently shut. I didn't know a heart could turn so cold.

Our marriage had unravelled as fast as a plate of oiled spaghetti, but left sticky dregs behind that stuck fast to the sieve. They had to be soaked and soaked again to break them loose—soaked, scoured and scraped again and again at the sink—with the salt from my tears.

It took an ocean of tears and all my strength to face my fear of a future without Angus. It took the patience and care of resilient friends and family to pull me through. I had pinned my existence to his—sought approval in eyes that had once reflected the youthful exuberance of lofty ideals. I had made his ideals mine; spent half a lifetime living up to them; raked over my soul to extract their full value; relinquished my soul to that purpose. I had idolised him—made a pedestal and placed him on it. When we aim to please, it is so often at our own expense.

With my dream of growing old with Angus dead, and with Amar busily making plans to move to Jakarta, I began to play with thoughts of moving to Yogyakarta to spend more time with Harto. I wanted to leave the scenes of my past with Angus behind. Images of us in happier days still haunted the cafes and cinemas; the streets and footpaths; the restaurants and shops; the buildings and the bridges and the parks of Brisbane. And while our family home had sheltered me through all the pain of his leaving, without Amar and his friends to care for, I didn't have enough reason to stay.

Now here I was a year later, bumping along the busy roads of Java in a white Toyota Kijang, with Pak Sungkar and Yana, on the way to see a house in Bausasran with Harto. The earthquake, the dental appointments for Saraswati, Harto's hookworm episode, my TESOL training, a year of teaching, and Amar leaving home bound for Jakarta were behind me. The house in Brisbane with its sweeping gardens, its orange-blossom scented breezes, and its weatherboard walls were a fading memory, but I held a faint hope that the house in Bausasran would hold a similar charm. A hope that another old house, in another country, would wrap the same warmth of that gracious old Queenslander around me. And I hoped to build a sense of security in a country busily rebuilding a measure of its own after a disaster that had displaced not one, as in my case, but many thousands of lives.

The earthquake that struck Yogyakarta on 27 May 2006, toppled schools, university buildings, houses and mosques—and also toppled stones from the stupas of Prambanan temple. Giant stones that made Yana's eyes grow wide in disbelief as Pak Sungkar sailed the Kijang past. The earthquake had, in less than a minute, created a Salvador Dali landscape, brushing slanted buildings onto a canvas land, which I saw first-hand a few days after the chemical burns to Harto's back had begun to settle.

A sports stadium in the south made Harto and I stop to join a group of others staring in wonder because it appeared like a sinking ship. But how can a ship sink on land? Without an ocean in sight the mind struggles to comprehend.

Television images I had seen in Brisbane came to life from the back of Harto's motorbike, as we rode at a putt-putt pace from Mount Merapi in the north, circled the city centre and surrounding districts of Yogyakarta then rode another hour to Parangtritis beach. Harto was still recovering from the hookworm infestation, the trauma of which now paled by comparison to the scenes we saw before us and I understood, with some regret, why he had not wanted any fuss.

A surrealist painting continued to materialise before our eyes. There were people sifting through endless piles of rubble that had once been family dwellings—homes with red-tiled roofs that had sheltered and protected. Traditional houses with traditional walls made from red, clay-fired bricks, trowelled together with black-sand mortar—but not enough steel supports to withstand a sudden force of nature.

The only buildings still standing strong were simple bamboo huts. They seemed to teach a poignant lesson about strength in simplicity and the peace of mind to be had in a less materialistic way of life. If only we could be satisfied with less.

We passed homeless villagers everywhere, women sitting on woven tikar mats, nursing children and their own shock, while others went about routine chores—hanging laundry on makeshift bamboo lines or squatting beside government-issue green gas cylinders to cook simple meals in woks.

Tarpaulin shelters had been rigged up in many places to provide shade from the hot sun, and the rudimentary comfort of a place to eat and to rest—a place to feed children. We passed a sprawling camp of UNHCR canvas tents in the worst hit area of the south, Bantul. The tents had been flown in and assembled by the army. Scattered around were boxes and bags of *sembako*—the nine groceries classified by the Indonesian government as essential. Nowadays these items vary but always include: rice, eggs, chicken or beef, cooking oil, gas, sugar, milk and instant noodles. Khaki uniformed soldiers had delivered these staples along with medical supplies. They set about dividing them up for the newly homeless with the help and compassionate hands of *gotang royang* groups and foreign aid workers.

At least, I thought, the weather would be dry for the next few months. It would be November when the wet season rains returned, if the weather could still be trusted. Early November 2006 was when I was scheduled to start a teacher training course in Denpasar, the bustling capital city of Bali. Harto was to leave his family for that month to give support. We had put these plans in place before the earthquake struck, because romance as much as daily life needs funds to put food on the table.

The earthquake had been sudden, causing upheaval and chaos in an instant. The mudflow slowly shifting sand and lives in the hourglass of time. As I wrapped my arms around Harto on the back of the motorbike that day the impermanence of all things and the need for courage to face that reality struck me forcefully.

Clearly, I needed to move on with life after Angus. I would have to put my fears on hold, and take a leap of faith into the ring of fire with all its volcanoes, hot mud and shifting tectonic plates. And in this landscape, I needed a job that was more portable than fashion.

"Saraswati insists that I come to help you in Bali, she will be okay for one month with her parents, and she will sleep as always with Bhima. Don't worry," Harto assured.

Bhima, who would later sprout tall and thin, was at the time a small chubby-cheeked boy, just turned five. In an old photo he is sitting in a black plastic bucket covered with foam and bubbles. His tummy is a wet balloon about to burst! His beaming smile has turned his eyes into slits. He looks like a laughing Buddha.

"Saraswati is very kind Harto; Let me send some extra money to help her manage while you are away."

"That isn't necessary Lara. She will be okay. I always give her the monthly wage you pay me. She can manage it better, and she will earn money selling *ronde* ginger tea with Mbah Salim, her mother, at the late-night stall near the palace—and she has many kebaya blouses to sew for a neighbour's wedding party."

"I would feel better if you let me help, Harto," I had insisted, knowing that he, with his Javanese manners, would refuse my first and second offer and I was determined to help with the family budget. The economic reality demands it.

"Lara, there is no need to worry for now. Save your money for study, so later you can work in Indonesia." That was Harto, with his practical bent.

27

The fact that I knew about the teaching course was a stroke of luck. On my second visit to see Harto I had by chance met a woman from Sydney. A fellow Australian called Evelyn. We became well acquainted over the weeks that we stayed at the Puri Artha hotel in Yogyakarta.

The Puri Artha hotel, with its Balinese architecture and frangipani trees, had been a happy discovery for us both—and for me a home away from home and a place for Harto and I to spend secluded afternoons together.

"Teaching English would be a more portable career than fashion," Evelyn suggested one morning at the breakfast buffet as we spooned servings of sticky-black-rice pudding into bowls.

At our usual table in the tropical gardens of the open-air restaurant she told me about a qualification I could get to change careers. She said many people used it to combine work and travel. It was called a TESOL qualification. I had never heard of it before.

"Don't you think it's a bit late for me," I frowned, cupping a small glass of sweet black coffee.

"Never too late," she laughed as she threw back her head and wriggled taller in her teak chair. Then as usual she fished out a small jar of Vegemite from her tote bag and scraped some of the salty black spread lavishly onto her toast. Her zest for life was infectious. We were close in age but not in experience. She was an independent woman—a seasoned traveller. I was a fledgling just out of the nest.

Evelyn was much taller than me, with an ample figure that she carried well. I found it impossible not to take these mental measures, having for years created clothing for clients of all postures, shapes and sizes. Pinned and darted—pleated and tucked. After we spoke, I pondered about a future that would involve grading assignments instead of paper patterns from size 8 to 16.

In fact, it was the colourful batik clothes Evelyn wore that first caught my eye—breezy and loose fitting. Evelyn came into my world in a bold blaze of colour.

"I refuse to wear dull-coloured clothes," she laughed, when I complimented her on her outfit. At the time I was wearing a beige dress with only a hint of colour in the silk scarf tying back my hair—happy in the camouflage colours that allowed these dressmaking observations known in the trade as figure analysis.

"They were made by a tailor in Jalan Solo, she enthused, and a few other things too. Would you like to walk there together?"

Evelyn called herself an Indophile. She said it with the clap of a laugh that made me laugh too—but also caused me to consult the dictionary later in my room. Indophile: a lover of all things Indonesian: culture, history and cuisine. I decided then to become more knowledgeable on those subjects myself—to take another step towards independence. I no longer had the straight 'A' husband who had been a walking reference book and translator for me for years. I made a resolution to learn as much as I could and immerse my thoughts in something other than the state of my marriage.

The next day I bought history books from Gramedia, the big bookstore in Jalan Gejayan. Amongst them, a biography of Abdurrahman Wahid, the former president better known fondly as Gus Dur—because when I read the first few pages in the bookshop, I couldn't put it down. But I was more drawn to books on traditional costumes, textiles, herbal drinks and spicy food, language, poetry, batik and wayang theatre than politics.

The books were heavy so I took a pedicab. On the way back to Puri Artha hotel it poured. Apart from the biography of Gus Dur, the new books were sealed in plastic to protect them from smudgy fingers; frustrating in the bookstore earlier but appreciated now.

The becak driver jumped down in his blue plastic poncho and closed the vinyl hood. He covered the front with a clear plastic sheet and continued to peddle into the driving rain.

"Mampir disini dulu, ya Pak, saya mau beli sate ayam," I sang out, practicing a sentence Harto had taught me. "Could you pull over here at Samirono restaurant, Pak, I want to buy some chicken satay."

"Ya Bu," he answered and wheeled across the traffic to a small restaurant on the side of the road. I bought two brown paper parcels of satay—a dozen sticks in each—and gave him one. He nodded politely calling me Nonya as he thanked me for my kindness. My happiness instantly multiplied by twelve.

Books and becak, driving rain and drifting thoughts…I must mention the teaching course to Harto when he arrived in the late afternoon, as he always did during those weeks, with a soft tap on the door of my second-floor balcony room.

28

When I flew back home to Brisbane, I scoured the Internet for information on how best to get a TESOL qualification under my belt. Hadn't Evelyn mentioned an Australian language institute in Bali? Yes, there it was! The Indonesia Australia Language Foundation. A modern building in Denpasar. There it was on the website, along with everything I needed to know about the course. I had been warned it was intensive. "Some don't make it through," another friend confided. She had passed the year before and was generous with her tips.

"You won't even have time to wash your hair," she wrote from Bali, where she had landed a job with a radio station. "Take folders and plastic sleeves," she said, "You will need a lot!" That turned out to be right. "Prepare materials, study grammar, look at phonemic charts before you come," she warned.

Phonemic what! My stomach churned with the nerves that come with unfamiliar territory. I put my fashion design skills into creating teaching materials that I could take already prepared. Surely instructions on how to sew button eyes onto cardboard puppets would be useful with so many verbs: to pin, to thread to cut and to glue. And the noun forms: a pin, a thread, a small cut, some glue! I stayed up late at night revising grammar I hadn't thought about since high school. I picked the brains of friends and family to help me with an application and a grammar test.

"Can any of you see a mistake in this sentence," I quizzed. Why is 'every day' sometimes two words and sometimes one?"

"Aah…I know the answer to that from my years as a typist," said one of the brightest. "As one word it's an adjective, as two it's an adverb followed by a noun."

"Thank you," I wrote in a thankyou email, beginning to grasp the concept. "And I need help with a letter about my working background and why I would make a wonderful teacher!"

In late July 2006, I was accepted into a four-week course to begin in early November. There was still plenty of time to prepare.

The four-week crash course in teaching turned out to be as intensive as the whole four years I studied fashion. If not for Harto and the red rice porridge that he spoon-fed me for breakfast and the rice dishes he prepared for dinner, I would never have survived.

"You must stop working and eat, Lara," he implored. "Later you will be just bones and I will be blamed."

"But I need to finish this paper, Harto. It's due in the morning, and I need to shower and wash my hair. I haven't yet thought of a good idea to engage the students. What if they're bored? Can you take this film to be developed for tomorrow's practice lesson, in front of a judging panel! Could you get large prints? I must look professional!"

"Leave them for now Lara. Come here. Let us bathe together. I will wash your hair." Oh Harto, my dearest love. How I would miss you close to me.

As soon as that hard-earned qualification was delivered into my hands, Harto rode off to have some copies made. These were stapled to job applications for him to post to schools in Java. Afterwards we returned the motorbike to the rental shop from where he had collected it a month before. We packed and said goodbye to the family and the staff of Rita's homestay and parted ways again.

"I will miss you, Lara. Promise you will come back."

"Thank you for everything, Pang. I will come back soon."
Harto took the long journey by bus and ferry back to Saraswati and Bhima. I flew home to the house in Brisbane and its big empty rooms. Amar was away on holiday in Jakarta. It was the summer that he met Alin—the love of his life—the future mother of his children.

--oOo--

In February, he came home again to tell me his happy news and that his plan to work in construction in Jakarta had met with success.

"We may be leaving home together then," I said. He threw back his head and laughed, patting a hand of encouragement on my shoulder.

"I just received an email with an offer to teach English in Sidoarjo, East Java, Amar."

"Take it, he said, and keep the wind in your hair, Mum. You deserve to be happy."

"Yes Amar. I doubt your father is ever coming back. We may need to sell the house. I will have to discuss it with him."

"From what I have seen, he isn't planning to come back soon, Mum, but I think we should keep the house," he said. "This is our family home."

I don't think it ever dawned on Amar that Angus and I being apart and living different lives meant that the family needed to break up. He was born with an optimistic nature—one that lifted me up. One I hoped never to crush.

"Okay Amar, perhaps he'll agree to renting out the house for now."

"Mum, isn't Sidoarjo close to where the underground volcano is oozing mud?"

"Yes, Amar, but the director of the language school I spoke with earlier on the phone said not to worry about the mudflow."

"Did she," he tossed back, like a tennis ball for me to catch, and then, "okay, that's good to know."

"She said the school was far enough away not to be affected, apart from the smell of sulphur on some days. She suggested packing surgical masks."

"It's standard to wear masks in Indonesia, Mum. I'm taking a few for the smog in Jakarta."

"Good idea, Amar. I hope the pollution doesn't aggravate your breathing. Pack some extra puffers," I reminded him, with a brow knitted in motherly concern.

"Don't worry, I'm big, Mum," he teased, leaning on my shoulder as if I was a lamppost.

"Yes, you are," I laughed, but inside I wiped a tear.

"The director, who called from Sidoarjo today, said the mud had raised the temperatures a bit but the school is air-conditioned."

"You'll be okay, Mum. You're a summer person," he reminded me as he pulled a long strip of photos from his jeans pocket.

"Check these out. Alin and I took them in a shopping mall booth in Jakarta." He leaned over the big black-granite kitchen bench, resting on his elbows as he waited for my reaction to the sepia prints. In the photos they're both making funny faces and laughing—his muscled arms around her.

"We are so compatible, Mum," he chuffed, like a proud male pigeon, all puffy chested. I tilted my head grinning at his photos fondly. Harto told me that pigeons mate for life.

"She looks cute and cheeky! I like her fringe, Amar."

"She's a tomboy, Mum; she only takes ten minutes to shop! She knows where to buy what she wants so we never have to look around."

"She's a very beautiful tomboy then," I grinned, infected by his happiness.

"Keep this photo with you, Mum," he chirped. "One day I will marry Alin."

"Perhaps you will mate for life, Amar," I sighed proudly, to his puffed bare-feathered chest.

"No doubt," he assured. But that is their love story to tell.

"Yes, I am a summer person Amar," I agreed, coming back to the previous topic, and luckily so are you. "Working outdoors on a building site in Jakarta will be steamy hot."

"Better to be too hot than too cold," he laughed, searching the fridge for a can of cold soda, as we happily sweated through the usual February heat wave. Both of us summer types.

"You better think about packing up your room, Amar."

"Sure Mum," he said ripping the ring off his soda can as he bounded down the stairs to his room.

"But I will speak with Alin first," he called back.

"Please say hello to her from me, Amar. I will look forward to meeting her very soon."

Amar's happiness cloaked the weeks before we left Brisbane with warmth and love as we both began to pack up a house filled with memories and, upstairs in the study, a growing collection of English grammar textbooks. Some of these I would send by courier to Harto.

29

My job interview had involved a question about how to teach a lesson on modal verbs—instantly flooding my brain with adrenalin.

"Do you mean 'must', and 'might', and 'could'," I asked, my nerves buying time to think? "I'm not really sure," I blurted into the handset, struggling to think of a good answer. "Maybe I would centre the lesson around daily activities. Things the students must or might do. Perhaps divide the class into groups and….ummm….I think I need more time to come up with something clever. I have a textbook with 101 ideas for teachers. I could bring it with me," I joked.

"Never mind," she said, "even the most experienced teachers need time to prepare."

That day, as I perspired through my interview with the Director of Studies—feeling too far away from Harto—I knew this was my chance of being with him. I said a prayer as I hung up the phone and sucked in a long breath of hope.

A few days after the phone interview, I was offered the job via email. I breathed a sigh of relief followed by an anxious one that had been on hold. There was another phone call I still had to make—a much-dreaded phone call to Angus. But first I called Harto. I had missed him terribly since the previous December when he had been my stalwart during the month of study in Bali. Every day he had prepared breakfast; ferried me back and forth to the language institute with endless patience and care; secretly set our watches ten minutes fast so I wouldn't be late to class; had massaged my headaches away using a Javanese pressure point technique. And on bad days when assignments threatened to overwhelm me, he had combed the knots and my worries out of my hair.

"I got the job in Sidoarjo, Harto."

"Congratulations Lara, that is good news."

"Thank you, Pang," I sighed, wishing I could squeeze him as tightly as I was holding my silver Nokia phone. "It is because of your help." The phone call to Angus later that day was not as easy to make.

Time has not faded the memory. I can still picture the old weatherboard house in the leafy suburbs of Brisbane, set high and well back from the street, hidden behind tall palms and surrounded by rambling gardens. Ceiling fans on low-speed thump their wicker blades through stifling heat. The gardenia hedges are in full summer bloom. Perhaps a flock of sulphur-crested cockatoos had up and taken flight from the giant fig tree near the back corner fence, as they often did when alarmed, their loud shrieks drowning out the swishing sound of distant traffic. On the low set coffee table in the living room, perhaps a vase of late freesias picked that morning from underneath the tall gazebo in the front garden—a feminine touch—a reminder of beautiful things.

Years spent taming the suburban jungle into lawns, bordered with mock orange hedges had seen the garden bursting with every shade of green, and sweet summer fragrance. Purple and white agapanthus line the long driveway, which swept up to a set of high stairs and onto a shady verandah with wide-open stained-glass doors.

Still, this tranquil vista did nothing to quell the butterflies stirring in my stomach as I nursed the phone and paced my breathing.

"Take another deep breath. Relax. Just breathe. Count in to four. Breathe out to six. Slowly. Count out to eight. One… two…. three…"

How is everything with the project, Angus?"

"Great Lara! A few hiccups here and there but that's to be expected. How are you, Babe?" And there he was still calling me Babe. And there I was still clutching on to it like a drowning child to a capsized boat.

"Good," I answered nervously, my thoughts reeling.

"I'm taking a job in East Java. I'm.... I'm.... wondering if it's time we sold the house and divorced?"

"Why are you being so dramatic Lara? I'm not planning to remarry and neither are you!"

"It's just... it's what... it's just what most people do when things don't work out."

"I've already discussed the house with Amar. He agrees we should rent it out since he is coming to Jakarta to work. You know it has always been his dream to renovate the old place one day."

The one thing that never wavered between the two of us was our love for Amar.

"Organise an agent to manage the house for now," he said, as if he was still in charge. All my resolve for closure melted onto the floor and I let him take control. That was my natural default.

"We need to hang on to property for financial security, Lara. No point selling up."

"Okay, whatever you think is best for Amar, but my teaching salary won't be much. If we don't divorce, I will need your continued financial support."

"Of course, Lara, that won't change."

--oOo--

A few weeks later I arrived at Juanda International airport in Surabaya to start a twelve-month teaching contract at an English language school, in nearby Sidoarjo. Harto and I flew in together from Bali where we had spent a few days. A uniformed driver, with a presence as polished as his shoes, was there to greet us. He was scanning the line of incoming passengers while holding a sign displaying my name in bold print.

"Excuse me, Miss. Are you from Australia?"

"Yes, Pak. I'm Lara. This is my friend Harto. He will be helping me in Sidoarjo. Thank you for meeting us here."

"You're welcome, Miss Lara. My name is Pak Agus. I am the school driver," he said with an enthusiastic handshake to each of us in turn.

"We can use this trolley here for the luggage, Mas Harto," he said using the term for brother. "Please wait in the pick-up area outside. I will load the car first and drive around to collect you. Please wait a few minutes," he called, manoeuvring the loaded trolley from the baggage carousel through the chattering throng of other arrivals in the airport terminal.

"Thank you, Pak Agus," I called out and turned to Harto as we walked out into the morning sun. "Thank you for coming with me, Pang."

Now those twelve months had almost passed. Almost a year of honing my teaching skills on four full classrooms of students, five days a week, had flown. Some students were boisterous, others shy, some full of questions and some with frozen tongues, but all had been a blessing to my new start in life. All of them as precious as the little girl sitting beside me that day in Pak Sungkar's Kijang, and as treasured as the gift of living part of my life with them.

I tap out a text message to Harto:

> We have passed Prambanan temple, Pang.
> Soon we will pass the airport.

Adisucipto International Airport, with its blue gate-lounge benches that we both knew so well. How many times had we parted there?

And a few weeks, or sometimes months later reunited. And with every parting, the same words repeated:

"Promise you will come back, Lara."

"Don't worry, I will come back soon Pang."

Harto sends a text:

Please show Pak Sungkar the way to
Puri Artha Hotel? I will meet you in front

Good idea Pang. Let's
stay there tonight

Okay Lara, I will organise
our usual room

"Pak Sungkar, Harto will meet us at Puri Artha hotel."

"Aah, I know it Miss Lara, near the Catholic university."

"Do you know the shortcut, Pak?"

"Iya Miss, turn left at Universitas Islam and then loop back?"

"Ya, Pak Sungkar, if not, we can't cross the traffic to turn right."

"It seems many people know the secret too, Miss Lara," he chuckles, checking the rear and left side mirrors, for a space to swing over in the lanes alive with taxis and trucks and darting motorbikes revving their noisy engines.

"Yogyakarta is swollen with students on motorbikes, Miss Lara. They come from every place in Indonesia to study here. This is where I met Yana's mother. We studied Law at Gajah Mada University together."

"I'm surprised to hear that, Pak Sungkar. That sounds very romantic."

"Ya Miss Lara, she attracted me with her passion in debates." This was news to me. After only ever seeing his wife Ira, struggling to swallow, silent, pale and ailing, this was indeed sad to hear; though it made Pak Sungkar's eyes light up in the telling.

"Perhaps Yana will follow in the footsteps you both left here."

"Inshallah, Miss Lara."

"My father was a lawyer too, Pak Sungkar. I sometimes wonder where my life would have turned if I had followed in his footsteps rather than my mother's."

"We can never know which turn our life will take, Miss Lara. Best to flow like a river."

"Ya, Pak Sungkar," I agree, holding onto my seat and Yana's leg as he swings sharp-left like a fish in the sea of traffic!

"We better tidy up these coloured pencils, Yana. Soon you will see your aunt and cousins," I effuse in a childish tone and then add in surprise: "Look over there, Yana, on the hotel steps. There is Uncle Harto waving his arm?"

"He looks happy," she smiles, wriggling higher in her seat.

"I'm very happy to see him too, Yana. And I'm so curious to see the house in Bausasran. If we rent it you must come to visit often. If not, I will miss you so much."

"Maybe Yana can stay with you if she studies later at Gajah Mada University, Miss Lara."

"That would be wonderful, Pak Sungkar," I agree, fondly pinching Yana's cheek.

"Can we park for a few minutes, Pak Sungkar, I want to show Yana the gardens."

"Please go ahead, Miss Lara. Yana will be happy to stretch the time with you. I will take a cigarette with Pak Harto."

"Hello, Pak Harto," he calls through the wound-down window.

"Hello Pak Sungkar, Harto responds, flashing a smile as he saunters over. How was your journey?"

"Very smooth, Pak Harto, and how is your mother?"

"She is recovering well, Pak Sungkar. Well enough for me to take Lara back to Surabaya by train tomorrow."

"Aah good, Pak Harto."

"Hello Harto, I've missed your smile," I say softly, stepping out of the car. But I mean, and he knows, I have missed his touch more.

"I have brought your helmet," he comforts. "We must go to Bausasran by motorbike."

"Of course, Pang, I was hoping we could," I smile, reverting to my princely term of endearment for him as he gently holds my eyes.

"Where is your luggage, Lara?"

"It was in the boot with Yana's cat but it looks like Pak Sigit, the security guard has beaten you to it. The luggage has gone and he's on the steps with Yana's cat."

"Don't worry, Lara, he will not let it roam. In Java cats have mysterious powers."

"So I have learned from Pak Sungkar. Can you wait a moment while I show Yana the tortoise pond?"

"Sure, go ahead, Lara, but you must hurry. Pak Yuda is already waiting for us in Bausasran."

"Yana, come quickly, I want to show you something in the garden." Taking her hand, we hurry past the gamelan orchestra in the lobby and out through the garden restaurant to a little pond covered with water lilies.

"Miss Lara, I can see a little tortoise on the stone," she gasps, squatting on her haunches to look more closely.

"Look there is another one Yana, slipping into the water."

"Oya Miss Lara, they look like toys."

"You're right Yana. They look like toys but they are little teachers too."

"I know Miss, from the story about the slow tortoise and the fast rabbit."

"Aah, you are so clever Yana," I cheer, deciding not to tell her the rabbit was in fact a hare. "But there is something else too."

"What is it, Miss Lara?"

"A tortoise's shell can protect its soft body."

"Like a house, Miss Lara?"

"Exactly, Yana. Just like a house. Now, we better run back so you can say goodbye to Om Harto."

"Miss Lara, can't we go slowly like the tortoise?"

"Oh ya, I say laughing, and take her little hand in mine. You are a fast learner Yana, much faster than Miss Lara. Can you teach me the word for tortoise? And what about turtle?"

"Turtle is *penyu*, Miss. Tortoise is *kura-kura.*"

"Papa. Papa. Don't forget the oleh-oleh for Miss Lara on the front seat," she calls to her father, as she slowly slides her feet back.

"Already. Already Sayang. I have given them to Uncle Harto. If you are ready, Miss Lara, I will take Yana's cat from Pak Sigit," Pak Sungkar, sings across as he grinds the butt of his clove cigarette into an ashtray on the reception counter.

"Please go ahead, Pak Sungkar, Yana is keen to see her big family." As they retrieve the cat I mumble to Harto from the corner of my mouth, "could you give Pak Sigit 5000 rupiah for his kindness."

"That is too much, Lara, and don't worry. I already gave him 2000 rupiah. He is more than happy." And he adds, as always, "you must be careful with your money."

"Goodbye Yana. Have fun with your cat and your cousins," I smile, squeezing her tight. "Goodbye, Pak Sungkar. Thank you for driving me safely here and please say hello to Tante Sarmini."

"Sampai jumpa! Sampai jumpa! Da-da, da-da."

Until we meet again.

30

Harto straps my helmet firmly under my chin before donning his own. Then he scans the sky for the sun's position and grins, "How was Pak Sungkar's driving, Lara?"

"He is a careful driver, Pang, but his eyes are not as sharp as yours. We almost hit a cat! Still, it was nice to feel protected from the weather."

"Don't worry, I will have my car-driving license soon."

"Then we must buy our own Kijang," I encourage, as he hangs the bags of oleh-oleh onto the motorbike's grocery hooks.

"Ya Lara, but first things first. We must meet Pak Yuda."

"Oh wait, Pang! I've just remembered the clothes for Galuh!"

"Later is okay, Lara. It's getting close to Maghrib."

"Never mind, I have some oleh-oleh and some fried chicken's feet and a head to give her."

"The feet are enough for Galuh," he frowns, before flashing a smile along with the words, "better to keep the head for me."

With that we set off from the Puri Artha hotel, and onto the busy streets of Yogyakarta heading south, as we have done many times before. Harto's eyes are as sharp as knives. I wrap my arms around him, feeling his warmth as we merge with a million others into the sea of traffic. Singles, other couples and whole families on motorbikes are zipping along the roads and around bigger vehicles coming and going in all directions. All my worries wash away and I think—don't wish for a car too soon.

We seem to fly over Jalan Dr Sutomo overpass and I see the Intisari Bakery Supply Store flash past, then an Indomaret grocery store and the family run Batik Museum— that I always mean to visit but so far haven't. Then we turn sharp right at a big intersection and soon we are passing Purwanggan, Harto's family kampung, on the left. Harto continues on and then gears down and turns right into a quiet side street. He slows to a putt as we pass a warung selling *soto ayam* soup, and the newly blacked tyres of his Honda 250 bump us gently over a few dusty dry-season potholes.

An old man with a map of wrinkles on his tanned leather face waves a friendly hand, as he wobbles along the road on his rusty bicycle. The bluish rims of his brown eyes glint when he gives us a toothless smile. He's wearing a neat, short-sleeved white shirt with a collar, and a tablecloth-checkered sarong. He must be on his way to pray at the mosque.

Three small bony-legged boys are taking turns to tug at the string of a torn paper kite stuck in the overhead wires. They turn as they hear us approach and their little faces, covered with the grime of a day's play, call out,

"Halo Missis. Halo Missis. Where you from?"

"Australia," I tell them, and watch three little sets of baby teeth reply with grins and giggles.

"Hati-hati, biarkanlah," warns Harto, as we sidle up beside them. "Just leave it. Meet me here at the same time tomorrow," he tells them. "I will bring a new kite."

And I watch again, as their eyes pop with disbelief at their luck in meeting the grown son of the legendary neighbourhood kite maker—the son who learned at the feet of his father the same clever craft.

"Lara, there is Pak Yuda waiting for us at the front gate," mumbles Harto turning slightly, putting a hand on my knee. And then a gentle reminder, "Don't look too enthusiastic, Lara, or he will raise

the price higher. It will be hard enough for me to bargain with him when he sees you are Western."
Harto stops in front of the house, pulls the key from the ignition and as we dismount Pak Yuda takes a few shuffling steps over to greet us. His face is old and drawn, his hair silver-grey, with a slight curl. On his head he's wearing a black *peci*, reminding me of President Sukarno in an old film reel, addressing the nation's people.

"*Selamat sore*, good evening, Pak Yuda," calls Harto, introducing me as the English teacher from Australia.

The butterflies in my stomach rise in expectation. Be calm. Be calm. Just BE, I say to myself. Sumarah! Surrender! Think of a cat!

I follow them both through the open double front doors and into the living room. I look up. And up. I see the big chandelier. Its glass beads lit with candle globes. Don't look too enthusiastic. Remember. Don't look too enthusiastic. Look at Harto and Pak Yuda with their hands calmly clasped behind their backs. Be contained. Be Javanese. Be like them. But I fail. I've already become Pollyanna, and I'm seeing the House of Chanel!

"Oh, it's wonderful, Pak Yuda. I love the high ceilings and the glass chandelier!" He looks at me and back at Harto a little bemused. And Harto, poor Harto, his face is a pale shock of disbelief. Like a world class boxing champion who has just been knocked out in a fight.

The living room is suddenly quiet except for the faint sound of ticking wood coming from the roof beams. Contracting. I search the floor for something else to say. Something to stop the rupiah notes Harto can see in his mind's eye, flying into Pak Yuda's bank account! I bite my lip. Think. This is business, Harto told me. Think clearly now. I run my finger slowly along a window frame and look up. Blow the dust.

"Perhaps a coat of paint to freshen the walls, Pak Yuda," I suggest. "And the floors might need a polish."

Harto's smile slowly reappears. He comes back into the ring. Cracks a knuckle out of habit. I can see his brain ticking over. I know him well by now.

"Thank you for the fresh towel, Lara," the fighter in him seems to tell me, and I know that his boxing gloves are back on and he's ready for round two.

Pak Yuda removes his smudged glasses and puts them in the pocket of his blue, batik shirt. Adjusts his peci. He walks ahead with Harto. I trail a few steps behind—poking my head into bedroom doorways as we inspect the house and grounds.

We step down into the kitchen and through it to a large pendopo in the garden. He tells us the house will include the gable-roofed garden shed beside it, complete with rusty metal doors that refuse to open, and a row of bedrooms, which I assume must have been the staff quarters for a rich family during the Dutch colonial days. He tells us we can use the collection of old brooms and woven bamboo baskets resting against the wall. The windows of an airy study look out over the garden, where there are two middle-sized mango trees. He notes they are just beginning to bear fruit. We follow him down a path of black sandy soil beside the garden shed, ducking under its rusty low set eves, brushing away some vines as we make our way.

My face lights up again when I see there is a large banana palm grove. Two of the trees are already heavily laden with big bunches of fruit. Pak Yuda says that he and his wife would be very happy if we could save these, and any ripe fruit from the mango trees for them.

"Yes, of course, Pak Yuda," says Harto, smiling broadly. "There is more than enough for a whole kampung." But under his breath he says to me, "Pak Yuda is pelit and all the neighbours know it." *Pelit* —mean with his money. Stingy.

"Thank you for showing me through your house, Pak Yuda. I will leave Harto to negotiate the price with you," I smile. "I'm looking for a house to rent for a few years."

"Sama-sama, Miss Lara, and the same to you," he nods shaking my hand. "Forgive me for leaving you now, but I must hurry to the mosque. Please take this key, Pak Harto, if you would like to look around further."

"Mathur Nuwun, Pak Yuda," nods Harto, respectfully thanking him in Javanese. "How about if I come to your home tomorrow morning with an older brother to discuss a contract?"

"Silahkan, Pak Harto. Please do. I will text message my address to you. Come around half past seven if that is not too early. My wife and I will be up before Subuh." And then, with a small puff of his chest he adds, "last month we performed the *haji* in Mecca."

"Harto, I love the house," I gush, as soon as Pak Yuda is out of earshot. "You were so clever to find it. My dream has come true, just as I hoped! These double doors and the carved-lace breezeways above the windows remind me of my house in Brisbane." Harto's smile breaks out all over his face. We're in the middle of the boxing ring and we've both won the match. He lifts me off the ground. We twirl in circles. I stretch my arms up to the ceiling. He's still holding me up, using all his muscle power. I laugh as I try to reach the glass beads on the chandelier.

"One more time, Pang. One more time." Finally, I manage to flick a glass bead, it hits the others and they all tinkle, and twinkle—like stars.

"Harto, put me down," I say, laughing and whisper, "the neighbours can see through the windows. There are no curtains."

"I don't care, Lara. It is not their business."

But I feel shy, so I drag him past the windows into a bedroom corner. He pins me to the wall, I breathe in his scent, run my hands down the damp sweat of his shirt, and for a while we kiss.

"Can we go to see your mother now," I say softly to him—melting. "I want to say hello and see how she is for myself," I insist, as I fish in his jeans pocket for the pearl clip he has stolen from my hair.

"Ya, Lara, we can visit her now. She will be very happy to meet you again," he says, releasing his lips softly.

And as I pick up my bag from the floor and we wander out through the double front doors of the green-gabled house—the dusk call-to-prayer bursts out from the mosques all around Bausasran and fills the sky, as if by the magic baton of a master orchestra conductor.

Allahu Akbar! Allahu Akbar! Allahu Akbar!
Allahu Akbar!
Ashhadu alla ilaha illa Allah.
Ashhadu alla ilaha illa Allah
Ashadu anna Muhammadan Rasool Allah
Ashadu anna Muhammadan Rasool Allah
Hayya 'alas-Salah. Hayya 'alas-Salah
Allahu Akbar! Allahu Akbar!
La ilaha illa Allah

God is Great! God is Great! God is Great!
God is Great!
I bear witness that there is no god except
The One God.
I bear witness that there is no god except
The One God.
I bear witness that Muhammad is the
Messenger of God.
I bear witness that Muhammad is the
Messenger of God.
Hurry to the prayer. Hurry to the prayer.
Hurry to salvation. Hurry to salvation.
God is Great! God is Great!
There is no god except the one God.

As we don our helmets again and ride the short distance to kampung Purwanggan to pay a visit to Harto's mother Ibu Daliyah, the falling dusk signals to the street lamps that it's time for them to switch on.

"Remind me to give your mother and Galuh and her girls the oleh-oleh from Solo, Pang. I have brought nasi liwet and serabi. And I have brought enough for you too, Pang."

"So, you have already learned the customs," he says turning, smiling, sitting taller as he kick-starts the engine. "Later you will become a better Javanese person than me."

31

The first time I met Harto's mother, two years earlier, she was waking up from a nap on the bare concrete floor of her house—a tiny woman with long, wispy grey hair pulled back from her high forehead into the soft coil of a *sanggul* bun. Wearing a traditional batik sarong and a grey brocade kebaya, she greeted me with the kind of searching eyes a simple cataract removal might have repaired.

Still stiff and stooped from sleeping she offered me her frail hand. She must have been over seventy by then but Harto couldn't say exactly when she was born. She had raised ten children in one of the tiniest homes I had ever seen, but the atmosphere felt warm. The outside boards and concrete walls were painted in kindergarten shades of green; the shutters trimmed in bright yellow. The low roof was a patchwork of rusted corrugated iron and slipping red tiles. There was a kerosene stove on the floor, the soot from which had blackened the walls. Harto was *anak bungsu*, she told me—the youngest child whose destiny in Javanese culture was to care for and comfort a mother. I wondered how she could have carried so many pregnancies and produced a final offspring that would turn out to be so tall, strong and robust.

Her house was sparsely furnished. On a cupboard beside the door sat a box television set and opposite a rattan sofa that sagged and was torn in places. We sat on the edge of it; smiling politely at each other and making small talk with limited shared language. Harto promptly brought some tea and, beaming a smile at his mother and me, tried his best to interpret. When it came time to leave, Ibu cupped my hands in hers and kissed my cheeks. I took some rupiah notes from my jeans pocket and pressed them into her palm.

"Sorry Ibu, I don't have a gift from Australia. Please take this rice money instead." It was just a few dollars. She looked across at Harto, then back to me, mouthing the words *mathur nuwun* for thank you, her fine skin wrinkling into a toothless smile. Then she turned again to Harto and I heard her say *Bismillah.*

"What is Bismillah, Pang," I asked him later.

"Bismillah," he said grinning, "It means in the name of God."

Harto had used the genteel form of Javanese, *Krama Alus* when addressing his mother that night—a high form of the Javanese language reserved for those who warrant the highest respect. The language of the Sultan's palace and the language of Harto's humble home.

I had never been through the alleyways that lead into the inner reaches of traditional kampungs. It isn't often outsiders are given the chance. At times I had to draw my breath, but I felt so privileged to be there. It was a long way from the land of the wide-screen television. The one that I had so recently left, but it was Harto's home and it was part of him. I fell for both.

We passed by a small, sunken-ceilinged room with a single kapok mattress on the floor and a wooden cupboard in one corner. Harto pointed it out as his and apologized for its bare state. It struck me in that moment that I cared about his life and the hardships he faced, and that our lives would become entwined. These were still the early days of our relationship. He hadn't yet found the right moment to tell me about his wife, Saraswati and about their small son, Bhima, but he soon would. When we were still drowning in a warm sea of affection, our ship sinking, floating its stolen treasure to the ocean floor.

I say affection because love came later, and it came in the split-second speed of a switch one morning. We were stealing moments together in the corner of a small café. The same day the Indian Ocean swelled a tsunami between Simeulie Island and northern Sumatra.

"Even when you are eighty years old and you walk with a stick, I will love you," he declared. Those words won me over. His faltering speech gathered together from his repertoire of English words was expressed with the nervous restraint of a man not given to theatrical displays. A restraint that could have held back a king tide. The tide of his increasing dedication to a duty he had taken upon himself—a duty to care for and to love me through to old age.

I drank those words in like a healing dose of jamu herbs, even though I never expected our relationship to last. We lived too far apart. But when the choice came to end it, I wasn't strong enough to let him go. Instead, I left my birth country and came to his. Thus, we were swept into the current of each other's fate, and the swifter current of Saraswati's, unaware of how she would suffer, and how we would suffer the loss of her in our lives and in both our hearts after I too came to love her.

But how could I break another woman's heart and break a family apart, especially after the painful collapse of my own marriage?

"Banyak orang yang berhubungan gelap," said Harto. There are many in affairs. But this did not assuage my conscience. And in the words of the Nobel Prize winning writer, V.S. Naipaul, it made for a society of half orphans. That was something I could not condone. I would never in a million years have wished that fate upon Bhima. And it wasn't a case of polygamy. Harto did not agree with that practice at all; in fact, he was against it. It was only that he wanted us all to be cared for and a certain amount of discretion was the only way.

"I love Saraswati," he said one day, "but I love you more." I believe he loved us equally in the way it's possible for parents to love all their children—love them for the differences they bring into the world. Saraswati and I had much in common but we were very different women, from two very different worlds.

--oOo--

The morning after I first met Ibu Daliyah, Harto took me to the beach at Parangtritis. Nyi Roro Kidul, the famous goddess of the South Seas is said to reside at the bottom of its perilous waters. We sat in tiny woven huts overlooking the ocean as the waves tumbled onto shore. There were people strolling up and down the beach but no one was swimming.

"Banyak orang tenggelam disini," Harto said as we watched. "What is tenggelam," I asked him. He threw back his head, pinched his nose. Did the act of a drowning person.

"Aah, many people have drowned here," I nodded.

"The waves are dangerous, Lara."

"Tenggelam," I repeated, "tenggelam, tenggelam." And for a while we gazed out together at the cliffs and the waves and breathed in the salt sprays of the southern seas, searching the misty clouds for birds of flight on the blue-layered horizon.

This was the way we communicated in the beginning. We learned from each other. I was trying to make up for lost time, lost love and looking for a place to belong. Harto had taught himself street English as a means to survive.

We had ridden to Parangtritis on his motorbike that day. His old red Honda. It was our only form of transport for the first few years we were together.

I had left behind the trappings of a privileged life: a shiny silver sports car with soft leather upholstery, and a rambling old Queenslander with feather-stuffed sofas and three hot water bathrooms. But the elements: sun, wind and rain, the senses: touch, feel, whisper, hear, taste, skin on skin, loving arms and laughter had all joined forces to wash away my recent past and win the case against those creature comforts. And witnessing the many layers of life in the kampung had opened my eyes to a world far different than mine. I could see there were riches hidden within it.

That first night when we puttered into Kampung Purwanggan on Harto's old Honda the atmosphere had been alive, and lively in the full-moonlight—and the lamplights. A few residents were coming and going on their motorbikes and scooters, dipping their heads politely as they passed. In the background the crackle of a radio playing Campursari music, and from someone's living room the sound of gamelan gongs, and the changing voices of a *dalang* puppeteer on a *wayang kulit* broadcast.

A group of children playing an alphabet song game on the ground in front of a doorway were falling about in spontaneous fits of giggles. There was the clatter of cooking. The wafting scent of mangoes hanging in bunches from a tree that had broken through a concrete path; the smell of jackfruit; garlic and coffee. I remember a plate of fried bean curd with fresh green chilies brought over from a neighbour. The generosity. The smell of jasmine soap from the public mandi mixed with the acrid smell of cockroaches that darted in and out of open drains like underground guerrilla militia.

Sitting here and there were the inhabitants in relaxed conversation, broken intermittently with peals of laughter, and for a while I had felt my worries wash off and disperse into the smoky night breeze with theirs.

--oOo--

Two years later, as Harto and I putter into kampung Purwanggan again on the same old Honda, it is a far more familiar place. The neighbours nod and greet us as we bump our way along to the tiny home where Ibu Daliyah raised her ten children.

"Pang, where is Ibu? The house is empty," I say, removing my helmet to peek through the wide-open door of her house.

"She is probably around the corner at Galuh's house, since Galuh has taken the television set."

"Never mind Pang. As long as your mother is not alone," I say sounding more and more Javanese, as I unhook the bags of food from the motorbike. Both wearing boots we tread a few metres more through the warren of alleyways that lead to Galuh's.

"Welcome to my home," sparkles little Rani from the doorway with her dimpled, dolphin smile—just seven years old and blessed with the same movie star looks as her older sister, Leila.

Pouting, she moans, "Your skin is so white, Miss Lara, like Leila's. Mine is so black. It isn't fair." She doesn't yet know that she is incredibly beautiful, and that it doesn't matter at all if her skin is darker than her two sisters.

"You're all alone, Rani. Where is your sister, Ninik?"

"She's gone to Leila's. The monthly *arisan* meeting is tonight. It's Leila's turn to organise the raffle and bring the cakes for all the mothers."

"The other mothers will be happy then, Rani. I heard that Leila's cakes are delicious. By the way where is your mother? I've brought serabi for her."

"She's standing over there, Miss Lara, watching you."

I turn around and there is Galuh with her cheeky grin and her pageboy haircut— flicking the blunt cut fringe from her eyes. She's leaning back on a concrete wall covered in moss, one hand behind her back the other holding a cigarette. Her legs are shapely like Harto's. I can see the muscles in them. She's wearing army shorts and tilting her head back as she breathes out a thick stream of smoke.

Harto's face is a plaster mask of disapproval, but I can't help smiling. I've rarely seen a woman smoke in Java.

"Good evening, Galuh," I call over to her and ask, "What news of you? How was the beach at Cilacap?"

"Cilicap was just fine, Juragan," she throws back, calling me boss as usual. "What news of you? It's been too long."

"I've been teaching English this past year in Sidoarjo, Mbak Galuh, but I will move here soon."

"That is good news, Juragan. You can teach my children to speak English too," she states with a toss of her silky hair.

"Ninik is already fluent, Mbak Galuh; and very confident. But I will be more than happy to help her with any English homework and for her to practice with me," I offer.

"I will come to work for you, Juragan. Don't forget me," she adds, grinding her cigarette butt firmly into the layers of flaking paint on the outside wall.

"I've brought some oleh-oleh from Solo for the family," I say, holding up the full bags. "There are two chicken's feet especially for you. And by the way I have some clothes too, but they're still at the hotel. Remember the black cargo pants I wore last year? The ones you liked. Maybe Harto can bring them tomorrow."

"Terima kasih, terimah kasih, Juragan," she thanks me, as if she's just pulled the winning number from an arisan lottery. The corner of her lip curls in a smirk of sibling rivalry at Harto.

"Where is your grandma now," I ask, turning back to Rani.

"*Simbah* is sleeping, Miss Lara," whispers Rani, her sweet dimples reporting on her grandmother's current situation.

"Wait a moment, Juragan, I will try to wake her," calls Galuh, sauntering over.

"Let her be. Just let her be," cuts in Harto. "She needs to sleep and recover." He is starting to look impatient. His set jaw and his brooding silence say it.

"Please say hello to Ibu and wish her my best, Galuh. I hope she can enjoy some of the *serabi* or a little *nasi liwet*. I will pray her strength returns soon."

By the time we stroll back to Ibu Daliyah's house, it's dark. As we sail the motorbike across the Code River bridge, I look up to see a swathe of stars twinkling in the clear sky like a Bethlehem Christmas, blanketing the red-tiled rooftops and leading us safely back to Puri Artha hotel.

32

"Harto, can you take the clothes to Galuh tomorrow on the way to meet Pak Yuda," I ask, as we dismount and remove our helmets.

"This time I will give them," he says, but his face is far from happy. "Be careful with your generosity" he cautions as we cross the street and climb the stairs to our room on the second floor.

"Yes Pang, I'll be careful. By the way we need to contact Aji. Ask him to come and work for us. And tomorrow could you take me into Jalan Malioboro? I want to look for a marble topped table and some rattan chairs at Mirota antique store. The house in Bausasran is so big. The furniture from the cottage in Taman Pinang will never fill it. And we need to go to the bank to transfer the rent money to Pak Yuda. Now that I've fallen in love with his house, I'm willing to pay whatever he asks. And don't forget we have to buy our train tickets for the Argo Wilis. I'm expected back on Monday for my last week of teaching, and to say goodbye to the students and teachers, and I need your help to prepare a speech for my farewell. Did you manage to organise a furniture truck? And remember to take the kites you promised to the little boys. And take the clothes I picked out for Saraswati to her. And give her my best, because I won't have time to drop in and see her or her mother and Bhima. Aduh! There's so much to do in just one day, Pang!"

"Ya, ya Juragan," sighs Harto. "*Santai aja* – just relax. "Think about everything else tomorrow."

"I'm not Juragan, Pang. Don't call me boss!" Though with all the demands I'm dishing out, I'm starting to feel like one.

Finally, alone and together, we shower away the heat and dust of the day from each other's skin with sponges lathered in foam from the hotel sachets. We're resting on the bed in the upstairs room that has become a home away from home. I bury my head in Harto's chest and breathe in the soap scent. The day has been a marathon, from the early morning start in Sidoarjo with Pak Sungkar and Yana, followed by the scenes of Lapindo mudflow, revisiting my past in Solo, seeing the house in Bausasran and dropping in to see Harto's family at kampung Purwanggan.

"You look tired, Lara," he says stroking my face.

"A little, Pang, but I have so many things on my mind. There's all the packing to be done in Taman Pinang; a farewell speech to write for school, and another thing, we must call Aji and persuade him to come and help."

"Ya, ya, later," he assures, fumbling around for the TV remote. "Rest your thoughts for a while." He turns on the television. An episode of Indonesian Idol appears on the screen. One of the female judges is dressed up in a glamorous gown. Her earrings are big gold hoops—reminding me of Roberta Flack.

A male contestant dressed in blue jeans is shifting his feet before the judging panel. His hands clasped behind his back to still his nerves no doubt. The orchestra music is holding the audience and me in suspense, while they consider a verdict. This poor boy's head must be swirling as much as the electric blue and violet stage lights. Surely his face—etched in a broad smile—must be aching.

"Why is he smiling so much, Pang," I ask. "The judges' criticism is so cruel."

Harto mutes the sound, clears his throat.

"He is smiling on the outside Lara. Inside he probably wants to crush them to powder."

Smiling broadly, he turns to kiss me, wraps me in a tight cocoon. He doesn't know that his own smile lights the room, lights my life, kills me softly. And the moon and the stars are the gifts that he brings to my dark nights.

"There is something you should know about Galuh," he says turning pensive. He tells me a story from when he and Galuh were younger. As he tells it he relives the hurt. He has two more stories involving her misdeeds. She has sinned against him three times and the cock has crowed. He has not forgiven her. He never will.

These three stories have formed a repertoire that is seared into Harto's memory as a warning, should he ever be tempted to soften towards her again. I was to hear these stories several times over the years.

In the first story, he was ten years old and she five years his senior. Each day Harto's mother would give him 15-rupiah pocket money to buy lunch at school. Rather than eat lunch he preferred to save the money, and when he had enough coins, he asked his mother to exchange them for paper notes until eventually he had five 100-rupiah notes. These he hid carefully in between folded clothes in his cupboard. Every day after school he would check his money was still there. One day he couldn't find it. Suspecting Galuh, he reported the missing money to his mother. She quizzed Galuh, who admitted she took it. Her reason? To enjoy. Galuh promised she would pay back the money but she never did.

The second betrayal happened after Harto started working in Jalan Malioboro. It was 1993. He was twenty-three years old. He remembered the date. The seventeenth of August: Indonesian Independence Day. He had earned 700,000 rupiah from a European customer for a large batik painting. He was so surprised by this luck that he told Galuh. She persuaded him to lend her the money saying it would help her to start a business selling rice and sugar from her home behind Ibu Daliyah's. She never gave the money back because the business failed. At that time, she had one child—Leila.

In the third story she asked to borrow money to buy a motorbike. Harto didn't have money so he loaned her his motorbike. Sometime later he asked, "Where is the motorbike?" She answered, "Still being borrowed by someone else." She had been persuaded by a paranormal to loan his motorbike as a guarantee to borrow money from someone for another motorbike.

"Friends said her money would grow bigger, but they were lying."

After a few months he asked for his motorbike back, but instead she asked him for more money. Three million rupiah. After that she said she would give Harto her new motorbike. Once again, he was conned.

He waited patiently for a month. The new motorbike still didn't appear. He realised she was lying, which made his anger build. When he went to confront her, she hid. Harto was already married to Saraswati by then. He had to walk to and from Jalan Malioboro in the heat every day for two years until he had saved again. Galuh always promised to give the money back, but she never did. "She always buys nice things instead," he said.

"Now I understand, Harto. I do. And I see her character is very different to yours. But I still feel pity for her. She is embarrassed to be poor, and it's more difficult for a single mother to earn enough money to live."

"She has a man with a lot of money who looks after her well. Don't worry, Lara. Her character is not good. She is egois."

Egois, like the English 'egotistical' means boastful and self-centred. And as in Western culture, is a quality not admired.

Later I hear from Galuh herself that she is the second wife of this older man, Pak Hadi, and that she loves him and he loves her. When I see them together, they look relaxed and happy. He has a distinguishing mole on his kind brown face. His cropped hair is grey, matching his brushy moustache. She tells me she gets along with his first wife very well. Pak Hadi doesn't live with Galuh but he is like a father to her younger daughters—and that's how Rani and Ninik see him. He stays at their house from time to time and takes them for family drives in his Kijang. Of this, Galuh is extremely proud.

After Galuh comes to work at Bausasran, she confides she is scared of Harto. She tells me this when she is in tears because she can't pay her electricity bill. Or she can't pay this or she can't pay that. I give her the money because I can see how stressed she is. The tears work. She pleads with me not to tell her brother. I'm not comfortable at all and I wish she wouldn't ask. Her wage is already well above average. Still, I give her the money, and I stay quiet, though I sense she knows how it pulls my loyalty from him to her.

33

"Do you still have Aji's telephone number, Pang?" I mumble, as the morning light filters through the curtains. My head, still buried in his naked chest, is full of thoughts.

"Ya Lara, I tried to call him while you were sleeping. He didn't answer."

"Could you try again now, Pang," I ask again and tease him with a firm leg lock. "I won't let you move until you call. I will use all my Juragan powers."

"We should eat the hotel breakfast first, Lara, before the black rice porridge is all gone,' he smiles releasing himself with a kiss. "I will try to call again while you take a shower."

"You're right, Pang," I concede. "The black rice porridge here is delicious. You always know how to win me over."

Harto reported over breakfast that he had briefly spoken to Aji. He would arrive around 'tanggal muda', which meant at the end of the month when he received his wages.

Most people in Indonesia are paid monthly so there are two important dates on the calendar. *Tanggal muda*, meaning the young date, and *tanggal tua,* meaning the old date. The young date is the happy date when pockets and shops and cupboards and stomachs are full. The old date is when people become resourceful. They might pick papaya leaves off trees to make vegetable dishes and fill up on more white rice with sambal sauce and put less protein on their plates—or live on *Indomie* noodles.

"Aji has lost his enthusiasm about the labouring job in Jakarta just as I expected," said Harto, "but he must learn about the world by himself."

"Well, it's wonderful news for us!" I said, scanning the breakfast smorgasbord for sticky black rice porridge

"Thank you, Pang, now that's organised I can relax. Perhaps I'll go to Martha Tilar salon next door for a massage and a manicure while you organise things with Pak Yuda."

"Good idea, Lara. You can enjoy some hours of relaxation. I will take Saraswati and Bhima to the mall. They asked for my help to choose new soccer shoes."

"Enjoy your family time, Pang and remind me to go the bank later. We need a deposit to secure the house."

"Don't worry, Lara, I will make sure Pak Yuda keeps the house in Bausrasran for us. And I will check the local price of antique tables and chairs in Mirota furniture store. You can choose something you like before we catch the train back to Surabaya."

Over breakfast Harto and I agreed to meet later in the front of Hero supermarket in Malioboro Mall. I would take a taxi there after Maghrib and we could walk to Mirota from there. He promised to take me to eat *gudeg sagan*, my favourite saucy chicken dish—though he said he may not have much appetite as Saraswati and her mother were cooking *opor ayam* chicken curry.

"Of course, Pang, they will be disappointed if you don't stay for dinner. They need some time with you. Please, apologise for me. Tell them I'll visit as soon as I'm settled in Yogyakarta," I assured, politely declining Saraswati's invitation to join.

--oOo--

Amid the sweet and soapy smells of the salon my thoughts returned to romance with the house in Bausasran. In truth she was in as much a state of disrepair as I had been. Her former tenants had long since left and small creatures had taken up residence in their place. Cobwebs hung in mesh threads from the ceiling corners, a thick layer of dust had settled on the windowsills and the cupboard doors in the kitchen had become unhinged. The tiles throughout were cracked in places and the walls were crying out for a fresh coat of paint. And…if the truth be known, the glass beads of the chandelier were looking around for the feather duster. However, these things could be easily fixed. I saw only what I wanted to see and I saw the things that Harto hoped I would see and be happy with; high ceilings and large airy rooms. And, through my rose-tinted glasses, I saw a glimpse of the same grace and charm that imbued the weatherboard walls of the house I had left behind in Brisbane.

Some houses wrap you in their arms, and like the old house in Brisbane, Bausasran was one and her arms were feminine, as if she was dressed in a fine brocade evening gown, as whimsical as the decorative panels above her doors.

Someone before me must have felt the same because I noticed, as I followed Pak Yuda and Harto around the grounds, the word RATU etched into a concrete garden path. My thoughts were at once confirmed. She was a ragged queen who had been abandoned. I would come to her rescue. Be her lady in waiting. Straighten her petticoats! Tighten the strings of her corset! And Harto—he could drive the palace carriage.

As the hairdresser massaged my scalp my thoughts moved on to the front garden, buried under a tumble of weeds. Star jasmine vines had crept up and over the pale green plantation shutters fixing them firmly to the outside walls and causing the paint to flake and fall. I would need Aji's help to resurrect the gardens so her rooms could be filled with fragrant flowers and through the freshly painted shutters I imagined, would waft the scent of night jasmine.

"*Saya bisa memperbaiki semuanya, tidak usah kawatir,*" Harto had said, sweeping an eye over the dust and cobwebs the previous day. "I can repair all. There is no need to worry."

But while I nodded, my designer's eye was noting things that could bring her faded beauty back to shine. And though Harto had proved he could patch a leaky roof, rig up a sturdy clothesline, polish new life into old possessions and had been crowned my hero in the snake and rodent-catching department, I felt this job could use two pairs of hands. That is why I suggested Aji.

Besides, Harto's strengths were more suited to organisation and negotiating deals. In this he succeeded beyond expectation. I agreed to rent the house in Bausasran from Pak Yuda at the discounted amount of 25 million rupiah a year, less than three thousand Australian dollars.

On top of this marvel, Harto would succeed in negotiating an affordable price for the marble-topped table and rattan chairs that I had dreamed of owning ever since I first sat in the library of Pak Suyono's home in Solo—all those years ago.

The tickets back to Sidoarjo on the trusty old Argo Wilis did not require any negotiation at all. There are some things in Indonesia with a set price. Train travel is one of them. We bought our tickets for the five-hour journey from the platform kiosk at Stasiun Tugu, situated at the northern end of the main street, Jalan Malioboro.

Harto had obligingly eaten a morsel of gudeg sagan from my plate, collected my bag from Puri Artha hotel, and left his motorbike under the watchful eye of Pak Sigit, the security guard. After dinner we caught a dusty pink taxi with balding tyres, low suspension and grimy windows the short distance back to Stasiun Tugu.

"The driver is lazy," said Harto under his breath. "He doesn't care about the dirty condition. No need to give a tip, Lara."

After he had paid the driver the exact meter amount and not a rupiah more, I nodded, "Yes Pang, but he was friendly and we are safely here. We must be grateful, though I hope the train will be cleaner."

"The train is always clean but there is no guarantee about the toilets," he grinned.

"Luckily, it's only five hours Pang. If we don't drink water, we can avoid using them," I laugh, continuing the light entertainment, which then reminds me to visit the platform toilets before departure.

"Be careful, Lara. The floor can be slippery."

"Ya Pang, but at least it won't be rocking and swaying like the train!"

Aah...the language of trains and all the nostalgia that comes with them: the rock and the sway of locomotive engines, as they puff and whistle along railway tracks, with their freight and passengers; the gentle rhythms of the coupling rods that reel through mile after mile of cinematic landscape. The verdant green plains and paddies dotted with people and mosque minarets and the mountain backdrops that roll past their windows—hypnotising.

But that night we didn't see any such scenery. Just our own tired reflections in the night train windows as the Argo Wilis train chugged out of Tugu Station. Harto fell into a sleep so deep that he snored, occasionally jolting me out of my dozing state and into thoughts of moving—of shifting our lives from Sidoarjo to Yogyakarta.

The air-conditioning on the Argo Wilis was, as usual, turned up to the coolest setting, which I had forgotten to prepare for with an extra layer of clothing.

Even though Harto had taken off his heavy black-knit cardigan to share as a blanket, I shivered in my summer person skin. Resting my head on the shoulder of this would-be-soldier I stayed awake sorting my thoughts while the train chugged and whistled through the night. I thought of Aji and how he would bring the skills he used to transform the garden in Taman Pinang, to the house in Bausasran.

34

Taman Pinang, Sidoarjo, East Java, to be precise, had been my address the previous year. A quaint concrete cottage located in a housing estate a few minutes' walk from the language school where I first taught English.

The cottage was painted a cupcake apricot-pink with decorative trims in cream and set amongst a cluster of banana palms that came with a large family of cobras. Harto and Aji had caught their fair share with hooked bamboo sticks, cementing their friendship from the beginning. They had swept and raked, and paved over possible entry points until the snakes slithered back into relative submission.

Harto had met Aji in the street one day soon after we arrived. The two became almost inseparable in the year that we lived there together. Harto fell naturally into the role of uncle and mentor to Aji, who, just turned twenty, was eager to learn about the wider world.

Aji was an itinerant labourer from a village near the oil refinery town of Tuban. He had come to work as a carpenter on a luxury home nearby, and that is where I first saw him.

He was high up on the scaffolding, barefoot and balancing two buckets of bricks. I was strolling home from the English school with Harto after a day's teaching. He was carrying my heavy bag; a simple act of kindness that lifted not only the weight of my books but eased the emotional baggage I carried.

Harto waved up at Aji as we passed and they exchanged a few words in Javanese. Judging by the grandness of the house and the concrete columns that joined its multi-levels, the owner must be very wealthy, I thought, and said the same to Harto.

"He is probably a politician," he answered, dragging deeply on his clove cigarette with a look that crackled as much as its flaming tip. "For sure, the money is from corruption," he smouldered, blowing a stream of suspicion out with the smoke.

By then I had known Harto for three years and come to rely on him as a buffer from the world—the wider world of Indonesia and the world of my recent past. But in order to spend time in his company I must abide by the rules of politeness in Java, and respect its philosophy of social harmony, set well above individual desire. In compliance we set up a separate bedroom for him and the neighbourhood politely accepted him as my employee.

Respectful appearances are important in Java and keeping face was just as important to me, providing a curtain for the full samsara of life to be played out in privacy.

Perhaps I was brushed with a touch of Javanese blood at birth, but certainly the character traits of my late August birth sign that instilled a deep need to keep things in order. As it turned out Aji was born in early September, a fellow Virgo like me and equally fond of a tidy space. I recognised him as a kindred spirit by the way he lined things up in neat rows.

I'd breeze in after the short walk home from school if I knew that Harto had summoned his help, confident of being greeted by sparkling windows and gleaming floors. Aji was whip-thin from the waist down and all muscles from the waist up, with big sure feet, and he knew how to wring a mop! He would joke that germs were afraid of him. "*Kuman tidak berani masuk,*" he would say, with a shy but mischievous grin. A glance around the house would find laundry buckets, pegs, scattered shoes and garden tools all back in their home groups, the daily chores done and dusted.

The construction of the small concrete patio in the back corner of the garden was one of the first projects that Aji and Harto cooked up together and I had given them creative reign, fully approving any effort to tame the jungle garden along with the snakes. For them to have made it look so picturesque and inviting was an added delight. It was the addition of two rattan chairs, bought from a second-hand-goods vendor, that set the patio off so nicely, along with two foxtail palms uprooted from the vacant lot opposite the security guard, Jamil's hut. Jamil's sharp eyes never missed a thing.

One rainy night he rescued me from a snake-sized worm. It had squirmed in under the front door and held me hostage with my toes curled, along with my mortal fear of worms, in the far corner of the living room. On hearing my screams, he had forced open the front door like a superhero and snatched up the wriggly intruder with his fingers.

"Never mind Miss Lara. This one is just a large worm, not a snake."

Gallantly holding up its rope body like a trophy, he made his way out through the front door, saying he would release it across the road in the vacant lot where the two tall foxtail palms once grew. By then the tell-tale signs of their removal were covered with weeds and the bleating goats that had grazed peacefully by the wire fence were no longer there. They had been fattened for the feast of *Idul Adha.* But on the day of the foxtail-palm relocation, they hadn't blinked an eye, oblivious to the tree thieves, and their own impending fate.

In my mind's eye, I can still see Harto and Aji with Jamil milling around the security hut—two tall, one short. Aji and Jamil's skin is bathed in sunlight and golden brown, Harto's strikingly darker. They are all smoking, as if inhaling palm tree removal strategies with each lungful of smoke and exhaling solutions.

There is a hum of low talking and nods of agreement. From the study window, I watch Harto and Aji pick up their tools and follow

Jamil into the vacant lot. Thorny wild scrub grows in patches up to waist height but at least the weather is dry, so they will avoid the big rainy season leeches.

There is a sound of digging in the distance and instruction calls. Soon they beat a path back and across the road with the upturned palms in tow. A triumphant trio jogging in military rhythm all dripping with sweat.

When they reach the front yard, they turn the trees upright and rest the trunks against the house wall. Ruffled green fronds sweep the roof. Then they brush down their shorts and transform into a cross-legged conference on the new patio.

After too many cigarette packets lie crumpled on the ground and emptied glasses of sticky lemon tea have begun to attract an army of ants, the shirtless trio stands up.

Armed with a rusty pickaxe, they take turns to dig the hard, dry-season soil. When the holes are deep enough, a team effort hoists the wobbly palms up and into their new homes. They are held in place with a tepee of sturdy bamboo poles. Two welcome patches of shade appear instantly on the newly laid turf, and I dream a small corner of the Majahpahit Hotel Garden has flown in from Surabaya and landed on the back lawn.

All of these projects had helped to sustain Harto for the year that he was away from Yogyakarta, his birthplace and beloved stomping ground, and the people he held most dear. That was something I did not bear lightly and neither did he, so he would ride back once a month on the treacherous single lane highway with his wages in tow. If Saraswati and Bhima must endure missing him at home, at least I knew they would be comfortable and living well.

"Aji will accompany you home after school while I am away," he would say as he donned his helmet. Harto and Aji: my makeshift family. One to share and bear witness to the life I had begun in Java —the other a channel for maternal instincts and care.

For twelve months, Harto's sharp eyes, along with Aji's and my ever-vigilant ones, had kept watch for wriggly houseguests—in the form of snakes, giant worms, fuzzy green caterpillars and confident centipedes. But this was a year of only mild and curious tension compared to those I had left behind.

I knew that when I said my final goodbyes to the concrete cottage in Sidoarjo it would not be the snakes I missed but Jamil and the residents of Taman Pinang who had protected me from them.

I would miss the garden that Harto and Aji had created with its tri-coloured hedges that had grown up in the black soil overnight, and the perfect lawn they had planted so patiently with small tufts of grass. And the sound of plastic Ping-Pong balls played back and forth on the street table they had rigged up from old boards.

I would miss the neighbours and I would miss who I had become with them: the English teacher who liked to walk the five minutes to school rather than ride even in the heat and humidity. The Western woman who sometimes waded home through deep muddy puddles after rain, just for the freedom and the innocence of it, who revelled in the simplicity that life had become—despite the snakes. The new neighbour from Australia, who sat feet up on the front step in the evenings to join in their gentle conversations and catch the cool night air. But the wind had picked up and changed direction, as it is wont to do, and soon I would find myself in another house with a different garden in Bausasran, Yogyakarta.

When the grind of steel on tracks finally brought the Argo Wilis to a gentle halt at Gubeng station in Surabaya, the sun woke up, and Harto woke from his deep slumber.

35

"Pang, I didn't sleep much last night, and I have classes all day," I yawn, as we climb into a Bluebird taxi. There's a strong smell of vinyl and the seats are still covered in plastic film. The driver speeds along the fast lane as if he has left his wallet somewhere and needs to retrieve it.

"Pelan, pelan, Pak." Please go slowly, admonishes Harto, "especially for my guest here from Australia."

"Oya, sorry ya, Pak. By your accent you are from Yogyakarta?"

"Ya Pak, Yogyakartan people are more relaxed than Surabayans."

After sorting out the driver, Harto, turning to me with innocent eyes asks, "Do I snore last night, Lara?"

"Maybe just a little, Pang, but it was too cold to sleep anyway."

"Not for Indonesian people, Lara. We can sleep anywhere."

"I had too many thoughts, Pang. There are so many things to do!"

"Just focus on teaching today, Lara. Let me organise everything for the furniture truck with Pak Jamil. No need to worry."

"Thank you, Pang. I will stay with Lundy for a few days. She invited me last week. She is staying with her relatives in the two-story house near the school. She can drive me to the airport in Surabaya. I will go via Singapore to extend my visa."

"Okay, Lara, tonight we can sleep together on the single mattress. Tomorrow, I will offer it to Pak Jamil as he asked to buy it. Then I will go straight to Bausasran with the furniture truck driver."

"Just give the mattress to Pak Jamil, Pang. He has been so kind." And so, with our plans in place, Harto went back to Bausasran the following day. I went to Lundy's relative's house with my crammed overnight bag and stayed until my contract ended two weeks later.

--oOo--

The house was titanic in size with two spacious levels to get lost in. There was even a portal window above the front door. The living room was furnished with Ottoman style couches, Persian carpets and the largest coffee table I had ever seen; square with squat crescent legs. Lounging around it on the floor were two university student boys with their heads in their laptops, emanating the quiet confidence that comes with class and privilege.

When I arrived Lundy's aunt, Ibu Ari, was relaxing on the sofa in a daster dress with her feet up watching daytime soap opera. She was surrounded with boxes and bags of cosmetics.

"Good evening, Bu. Thank you for inviting me to stay," I say, scanning the high ceilings. "Your house is so lovely."

"Good evening, Miss Lara, you're very welcome. I'm happy to meet you. Lundy tells me you were a fashion designer in Australia before."

"That is true, Ibu Ari but now I enjoy teaching English more. Besides I would rather grow my collection of Indonesian kebaya blouses and daster dresses like yours, than design clothes these days," I laugh, feeling more and more dislocated from those designing days in Brisbane.

"Then we must go shopping in Surabaya before you go to Yogyakarta, Lara. Lundy can drive us, ya, Lundy?

"Ya, ya, Tante, for sure we can."

"Can we look for some dresses with the same butterfly pattern as yours Ibu Ari? It's very pretty."

"There are many Lara, don't worry. By the way have you eaten? Lundy, please take Lara to the dining table first. Help yourselves to Ibu Siti's hot and spicy sambal with the fried eel I bought from the market today. It's very delicious."

"Thank you, Ibu Ari," I smile. "I've never tasted spicy eel!"

Following Lundy to the dining room she tells me with a brush of her hand, "Tante Ari is bored with my uncle constantly away at sea. She started pyramid selling those beauty products for something to do."

When our hunger is sated with hot chilli eel, we climb the stairs to the second floor. She shows me to a large ensuite room. There's a strong smell of camphor coming from an ornate teakwood wardrobe.

"Don't be surprised if Tante Ari wants to practice a facial on you," she laughs.

"So, what does your uncle do, Lundy?"

"He's a merchant sailor, Lara, he's rarely home. That's why Tante Ari has so many staff. So, she's not lonely."

"That's one of my favourite things about Indonesian culture, Lundy. Whether rich or poor it seems you never have to live alone. I prefer this kind of group culture to the individual one of the West."

"Yes, Lara, but women shouldn't settle for married men," she says, shaking her strong-feminist head. "I'm still not happy about your situation."

"I know, Lundy. But I'm not taking the risk of marriage again."

"Lara, Lara, you deserve better for yourself," she admonishes, taking a sip of her hot lemon nightcap shuffled in on a tray by a timid young male *pembantu*.

"How about you Lundy? Your own affair is secret," I remind her, relaxing into the daybed on the balcony.

"That's true, she admits, but my situation is different. I'm Muslim and he's Catholic. Until one of us agrees to change religion, neither family will support our marriage. I'm almost thirty years old.

Soon his parents will find him a Catholic wife. But at least with my job as head teacher, I'm financially independent," she sighs, looking the part in her black business skirt, her crisp white shirt, her court shoes and her prescription glasses.

"I love him but I don't want to give up my whole life," she assures me.

"Don't worry about me so much Lundy. And please visit me in Yogyakarta."

"Of course, I will visit, Lara."

"Good! We can go to karaoke together. I'll miss you too much if not!"

"True, Lara. No one else can sing 'Yesterday' like us!"

"We must have a farewell karaoke next week then, Lundy. After all the student parties."

Farewells with the students mainly took the form of small parties in the classrooms, and karaoke nights. Classes of students squeezed together on the hard vinyl seats along the walls of the cubicles that made up the thriving family entertainment centre next door–singing at the top of lungs into shared microphones. Sometimes dancing. Always laughing.

On my last day there were speeches, and in the teachers' room plates of sweet cakes and pink coconut drinks. Later that night a shared meal and reminiscing with my first and favourite class of university students. Then photos—and more photos. "*Untuk kenangan, Miss Lara.*" For souvenirs! The little ones made enough glitter cards to fill a small shoebox. "I am Reza Miss, do not forget about me. I am Vania, I will miss you, my teacher." These and many others all signed with hearts. "We will very miss you," they cried. And I would very miss them.

After two weeks of hospitality, very spicy food and a few facials at Tante Ari's house; a weekend shopping trip into Surabaya to buy batik as promised and nightly heart-to-hearts with Lundy on the upstairs balcony before bed, she drove me to Juanda airport in her trusty old Kijang. In my tote bag, I had a ticket to Yogyakarta via Singapore.

"Thank you for everything, Lundy, and for your friendship. And please thank Tante Ari once again for her kindness and for all the cosmetic samples!"

"Ya, Lara, and say hello to Harto and Aji. Let me know when you are safely at the house in Bausasran."

"Sure, Lundy. Harto has already set up the furniture from Taman Pinang and Aji will arrive very soon to help with repairs."

"*Sampai jumpa* Lundy. Thank you for a wonderful year. See you in Yogya soon! *Da-da, da-da. Da-da, da-da!*"

Part Three

36

When I arrived in Yogyakarta later that evening, Harto had already unloaded the furniture from Sidoarjo. To my delight he had arranged the marble-topped table, along with the four rattan chairs I had bought from Mirota furniture store, under the big front windows. I made up our bed with a set of fresh cotton sheets and we slept soundly in each other's arms—the first of many peaceful nights at the house in Bausasran.

When Aji arrived the following morning, I was in the living room unpacking the last few boxes of household goods freighted with the furniture from Sidoarjo on a clunky, red, tarpaulin-covered truck. When I looked up and caught sight of Aji through the curtainless windows my welcome smile retracted of its own accord. His eyes were downcast so he didn't see the knitted brow that took its place. His face was hollow; his wide cheekbones more prominent than before; the square shoulders he had always held back now slouched over a sunken rib cage. How could Aji have come to this?

"In Jakarta his money is not enough to make full the stomach," fumed Harto under his breath as he hung his helmet on a hook in the pendopo and waited for Aji to trail in. Harto had pillioned Aji from Tugu Station, where the punctual Sanjaka train had deposited its passengers with military vigour. Aji, by contrast, looked defeated. A gaunt figure in his army shorts, but somehow, he still had style.

Style is a quality that cannot be bottled and sold like champagne. Style is an inborn thing, and Aji had it in spades. Two simple things stood him out in a sea of sameness: a sleek strap of liquorice black hair and an almost imperceptible diamante stud pierced into his nose.

Harto's words, out of Aji's earshot, had expressed his anger. They were followed by a softer tone as Aji entered the pendopo.

"Rest here, Mas Aji, I will bring some food," he comforted, disappearing on foot. Minutes later he was back carrying a plate piled high with rice, vegetables and tempeh from the warung next door.

Aji had arrived from Jakarta with few possessions; a prayer rug tucked under one arm and a small backpack of clothes. After he devoured the meal, he fell into a deep sleep. He slept on a tikar mat in the cool shade of the pendopo and woke at dusk to the sound of Maghrib prayers. Then he slept again until Isya prayers and the stars were out. Harto made some sweet tea and took two steaming glasses out to join him. They sat together cross-legged on the cool, tiled floor and chatted as they smoked clove cigarettes into the night.

I retreated to the sanctuary of the big floor cushions on the Persian carpet, leaving them to catch up amid the curls of smoke and the crackling of slow burning cloves.

Later that night, I learned from Harto what had befallen Aji in Jakarta. He had laboured long and arduous hours in the relentless heat and humidity. At night he had slept on flattened cardboard boxes in the dirt and debris of the building site. Like most labourers who come from villages, he was relied upon to send most of his wages home, but Aji could barely meet his own needs let alone those of his family. The friend who had promised him a good wage was corrupt. He kept the greater part of Aji's small wage.

Those last words hung in the darkness until we fell asleep, sealing themselves into a pact before we woke. A promise that while Aji lived with us his stomach would be full and his bed soft.

He slept on a bedroll on the floor that first night, borrowed from a neighbour in exchange for a clove cigarette. The next morning Harto and I rode to the furniture stores. Later that afternoon a flatbed truck delivered a thick foam mattress and some pillows. Harto deposited them proudly on the floor of Aji's new room along with a colourful set of hibiscus-patterned sheets.

"These will be more comfortable, Mas Aji," he said. "You will sleep better. Tomorrow we can start the repairs."

The following day under Harto's supervision, they both set to work. All the paraphernalia of a new painting project began to appear. An assortment of canvas drop sheets were carefully spread out over the tiled floors, along with a few paint-speckled planks and a pair of bamboo ladders. The two had reclaimed these useful things from a pile of rubbish that others had left behind.

Over the next few weeks, Aji whitewashed the smooth cement-plastered walls. As the house took on a fresh new look, the Aji I had known in Sidoarjo began to re-emerge in shy smiles that appeared more often.

Soon after, Harto bought a rice cooker from Progo, the big warehouse behind Jalan Malioboro, where you could waste a whole day comparing floor to ceiling plastic tubs in various shapes and sizes or testing the quality of woks and fry pans.

Then he went to the *sembako* supply store and bought a twenty-kilo sack of white rice to compliment the brown paper parcels of street food we were consuming.

Frequently he would bring home pieces of grilled duck garnished with cucumber slices and sprigs of basil, or chicken satay sticks with spicy peanut sauce–until I began to fret about the high fat content and miss fresh salad. Sometimes he would bring plastic bags of *ronde,* hot ginger drinks, laced with sugar syrup and sticky rice balls from Saraswati's mother's stall at the late-night markets. Aji sometimes ate with Harto and sometimes alone but never with me. He knew his place in the scheme of things. I was still learning mine.

After I started teaching at the school the following week, I took to spoiling Aji with deep-fried gurami fish. Harto and I would ride out to my favourite restaurant on the north ring road to buy it.

The neon lights of Cianjur seafood restaurant were hard to resist and the décor appealed to my romantic eye. It was palatial in size. Antique ceramic plates and local history in sepia prints covered the walls. We ate there often after my classes had ended for the day, demolishing a plate of barbequed fish between us. A whole succulent fish was served with baby kailan leaves, a delicious relative of the brussel sprout. Bowls of fresh sambal sauce (which made Harto's forehead bead with sweat) along with steaming baskets of fluffy rice would be brought to the table as soon as we sat down. This efficient service was not lost on Harto and the high standards for discipline he held in that regard.

He would claim the head and eyes of the fish and take his time to suck the bones clean. He always put the body and tail on a separate plate for me. I would eat half and push the plate towards him insisting he finish it. We were both considerate like that. Not a shred of flesh was ever wasted and none of the expense. Families came from all over Yogyakarta to feast on Cianjur's famous menu. The owners must have sold a trawler's worth of fish a day.

Aji's wide-cheek-boned face would flush a little as he stooped politely, accepting the flat cardboard box containing his. Then he would tread softly barefoot over the spotless kitchen tiles and wander out and down the garden path, swinging a kerosene lamp, to a quaint little tin-roofed shed beside the banana grove. Perhaps it reminded him of his village near Tuban. But I can only assume that is where he sat to eat as I never followed, taking account that I was foreign to him and he was naturally shy.

Gradually the meat that had disappeared from Aji's ribs in Jakarta began to return until, from the waist up, he was all muscle again, just as he had been when he mopped the floors in Taman Pinang. But below the leather belt that held up his baggy army shorts his hips and legs remained as stick thin as they had ever been.

After Galuh came to cook for us we didn't go to Cianjur seafood restaurant as much. She took up her new position as chief of the kitchen the day after Ibu Daliyah's funeral. She came because Elang had persuaded me, against Harto's wishes and all his warnings. Nevertheless, her cooking filled the house with homely aromas and the hot sizzle of palm oil she used to fry the food.

37

Not long after we moved into the house in Bausasran Ibu Daliyah's health began to decline. She'd had another fall and was confined to bed. During those first weeks, while I sorted through the boxes from Sidoarjo and Aji painted the walls, Harto would come and go to kampung Purwanggan, with a distracted frown and a cigarette smouldering between his restless fingers. "If my mother dies it will be a great loss for me," he fretted.

Early one morning Aji's soft tap on the bedroom door roused us both from sleep. Harto jumped out of bed to see to the matter. Then I heard a mumbled exchange in Javanese.

Aji had received a message from Purwanggan. Ibu Daliyah's time was near. I had never seen Harto pull his jeans on so fast. I didn't see him again until the following day at the funeral.

By coincidence, Amar and Alin had come from Jakarta for their first visit. The three of us had been out browsing the shops along Jalan Malioboro in search of headscarves the day before.

Alin wanted to buy some kerudung scarves as oleh-oleh gifts for her mother and sisters. And I had not resisted adding another batik-patterned one, in soft silk georgette, to my collection. Little did I know the following day, I would wear it to a mother's funeral; or that Alin, beautiful Alin–with her model's vanity bag full of make-up–and her suitcase that contained a prayer rug alongside her skinny jeans and heels, would help me to choose a modest dress from the new teak wardrobe in the bedroom, and arrange the scarf over my head and around my neck in the same glamorous style as hers. Or that

Amar and Alin and Aji would wave me off across the road and into the alleyways that lead from the house in Bausasran all the way into kampung Purwanggan to where Ibu Daliyah, wrapped in a white *pocong* cloth, was laid out in her open coffin in the front room of the tiny house where I had first met her.

On the night that Ibu Daliyah passed away, Amar and Alin and I were watching a performance of the Ramayana ballet in the same amphitheatre where I had first seen it with Harto.

Halfway through the performance rain began to spit. Not enough to make the actors or the audience worry too much. Moments later, I received a text on my silver Nokia from Harto. The message read:

> *Yang saya paling sayangi telah pergi untuk selama selamanya*
> The one I had most loved has gone forever

"Amar, I have sad news from Harto."

Amar answered with a comforting hand on my back. "Alin and I know, Mum. We both had the same strange sensation."

It was just after 9.30 p.m.

I swear, and Amar will swear, and so will Alin that the moment I relayed the message the sky opened up and rain pelted down in sheets and began to splash our faces. The cast of actors hitched their sarongs and made for cover. We hurried after them with the rest of the audience. By the time the crowd had reassembled inside, we and everyone else were soaking wet. Of course, the rain may have been just a coincidence but it didn't feel like one. Amar and Alin would say the same. The rain felt like tears from heaven.

Ibu Daliyah passed away on 21 May 2008. The date was painted in white on the wooden stake that marked her grave for a thousand days. The same date was later inscribed on the headstone erected to replace it. In between, there were traditional selamatan gatherings where family and friends prepared special foods to share and to pray for the release of her soul. Following tradition, the first selamatan was held on the seventh day after her burial, then forty, and then a hundred days, then each year on the date that she died for three years until a thousand days had passed.

After the funeral, I kept the scarf I wore in a drawer underneath a cheval mirror in the bedroom. It had become a shawl of sadness. I knew I would never be able to wear it without the weight of grief I felt for Harto.

Seven years later another scarf of the finest wool would be laid to rest beside it. And still long after, at times when Harto was deep in thought—his eyes distant—he would ask, as if to check, "Lara, do we still keep the scarves? "And I knew where his mind was drifting, because I knew the two scarves he meant, so I would bring them to him.

"Here is Saraswati's, Pang. The one the women wrapped around her face." Then I would kiss his forehead softly and tell him not to worry; that I would always keep them safely. And so, he breathed in her scent and for a while she was still with him.

38

The cheval mirror was an antique restored by Aji after it arrived with a truckload of furniture that Harto's friend, Wanto, had delivered from Semarang not long after we moved in to the house in Bausasran. He had attended Ibu Daliyah's funeral too, and that is where I first met him. Wanto was short in stature, but on the inside he was tall.

He was a confidence man. As much a born entertainer as the concert pianist Liberace, though he couldn't play the piano like him; or any other musical instrument for that matter. It was his vibrant personality that was as lovable. He wore large gemstone rings of tiger-eye and jade on most of his fingers and weighted his neck and wrists with ropey silver jewellery.

The only thing that kept the theatre of him in check was the fact that he was beginning to go bald and didn't want to show it. When his scalp began to shine through enough to draw attention, he took to wearing colourful skullcaps. Harto would tease him, telling him he should plant durian or papaya trees on this desert wasteland of his head. He would reply saying that he wore them for his wife who made them because she liked to crochet.

When I finally got to meet her, I was surprised. She was so shy and frightened of me she hid in the bedroom. She was the polar opposite of her gregarious and embellished husband. And he was the opposite of Harto, who, apart from a couple of sturdy second-hand wristwatches—and the new one I had brought from Brisbane—was not at all interested in body adornment. But they were as close as any best friends could be.

Funny how most people have at least one friend who is there to carry them through life's ups and downs. In this regard Harto and Wanto were there for each other. On the day of Ibu Daliyah's funeral, I noticed he came to sit for a while with Harto and Elang outside the room where their mother was laid out. I noticed how solemn he was throughout the prayers and proceedings, but when we all filed back to Bausasran later, his smile gleamed as if in competition with the lights in the chandelier.

"This man here," Wanto told me, in fluent English and with a theatre actor's flamboyance, "I owe my life to this man Harto. To me he is the best father. He took me off the street and taught me everything I know."

This was of course, a little far-fetched, but Harto had in fact helped him a lot. They had first met in Jalan Malioboro, the stomping ground for the dealers who sell batik paintings to foreign tourists. Harto had taught him the ropes and it was because of this that he loved Harto. He was in awe of his toughness and his commanding silence; a subject of Harto's royal court.

Wanto had worked in Bali before he met Harto and that is where he acquired his broad bank of English vocabulary, which was boosted by an obvious natural talent for languages.

He had worked as a machinist in the busy streets of Legian Beach in Bali, sewing leather shoes and handbags for tourists on a porch-sized pendopo, but anyone could see he was meant for bigger stages.

For all the time I knew Wanto, he could never do enough for me. He seemed to love me as much as he loved Harto.

"Whatever you need, Mas Wanto will find it, Lara," Harto would say with a look of paternal pride. "He has business connections everywhere."

Wanto became my Aladdin's genie, granting all three of my wishes for the house in Bausasran. And to my surprise and delight, with a speed just as astonishing!

39

My first wish was for a house filled with traditional Javanese furniture. Less than a month later that wish was granted when a mud-splattered truck filled with teak furniture arrived one bright Saturday morning with Wanto in command.

The first piece to take up position was a tall bookcase with glass doors. Four barefoot wiry-muscled men shimmied it into the living room. One, who appeared to be the leader, was so skilled he was able to call instructions while gripping a clove cigarette between his lips and smoking it right down to the butt with no hands.

The four furniture lifters had appeared as if by magic, but in fact had accompanied Wanto from the northern port city of Semarang, famous for its teak furniture factories.

The cupboard complemented (very pleasingly I thought, as I watched them place it) the plant green and madder red Persian carpet that Harto had rolled out on the living room floor.

Then in a blink the four men disappeared, bowing their way out through the kitchen to reassemble in the pendopo and await further instructions from Wanto. And to drink some iced lemon tea from the glasses that Aji had prepared.

In order to provide these refreshments, Aji had been forced to divert his attention away from a small box television set, alive with the broadcast of an Indonesian soccer match.

With each goal scored and the raucous cheers from the troupe of men and Wanto, the temperature under the pendopo began to heat up. I made my way out to the cool shade of the front garden to wait for Harto.

"Hi Pang, I'm relieved to see you! Can you be Juragan today," I plead, as soon as he rides in on his Honda. Harto is surely the only man in Indonesia who is more interested in flying pigeons and making kites than watching soccer.

"Could you have the *tukang* unload some of the furniture into the garden shed, Pang? Aji will need to stain a long kitchen table."

"Ya, Juragan, don't worry I can organise everything," he says, removing his red helmet.

"Don't tease, Pang, I'm not Juragan."

"We are both Juragan," he teases, with a smile that wants to escape the sun.

"Look Pang! We don't have shadows," I exclaim, trailing him as he wheels the Honda down the driveway and into the garage. "The workmen will be exhausted lifting heavy furniture in this heat. There's a big day bed and bookcases, some carved chests and a wonderful antique writing desk. The largest piece is a wardrobe. Surely it will take ten men to lift!"

"Don't worry Lara, they are used to hard work. Later they can enjoy goat satay," he reassures.

"Good idea, Pang, and please give them a tip."

"Just small money, Lara, or your money will soon be finished."

"Oh, and one more thing, Pang…could you ask Saraswati to come here later if she has time? I want to ask her about making some curtains for the front windows, and to offer her the small kitchen table from Sidoarjo. We won't need it now."

"Saraswati is watching the soccer match today with Bhima. It won't be easy to pull her away from the television, Lara."

"Oh yes, of course, Pang. I've seen how excited she gets over the soccer. Watching Saraswati jump up and down, pulling her hair and the hem of her daster dress is more entertaining than a grand final. She becomes all of the players!" I laugh.

"Bhima is playing soccer after school now, Lara. He has inherited the same obsession as his mother."

"Between Bhima's drum band practice and soccer, and her wedding kebaya business she is so busy, Pang. Maybe we should buy some ready-made curtains."

"True, she is always busy Lara, but she will be more than happy to sew curtains for you."

"Well, there's no rush if we're not seen kissing in the living room. I don't want to be a subject of the neighbours' gossip."

"Don't worry Lara. They will be happy if you are happy."

"I'm very happy with the furniture from Wanto, Pang. Every piece is perfect."

Not believing my luck, I had agreed to buy all the furniture that Wanto brought for me to peruse, because every piece seemed made for the house, and because the price was so much lower than expected. The furniture had arrived from Semarang in a similar truck to the clunky red one that had lugged our household goods from Taman Pinang. At the end of the day after all the furniture had been wiggled into position, and many cigarettes smoked, Wanto reversed the truck and goat-satay-sated men out of the driveway. The truck clunked its way down the street, turned right and drove over the Code River Bridge. Then with a last puff of diesel smoke it disappeared into the bustling streets of Yogyakarta. Like magic.

It took Aji another week to sand and oil the kitchen table and chairs because he was meticulous by nature. By then the soccer season had ended. During those days in the garden shed, with the doors wide open, he whistled, fully absorbed in his work and focused.

--oOo—

My second wish surfaced soon after the furniture had settled into place and the walls were freshly painted. This wish arose not as much from necessity but from a daydream I had while looking out over the front garden after all the weeds had been removed by Aji and replaced with small tufts of grass. With the tufts quickly joining together to become lawn, just as they had in Taman Pinang, I envisaged a collection of decorative ceramic pots.

Sadly, the giant pottery urns I had admired in the village of Kasongan, on my travels with Santo were priced well above what I could afford.

"Harto, could you ask Wanto if he knows where to find ceramic garden pots like the ones in Kasongan?" I suggested.

In the flash of a week, Wanto materialised in the driveway behind the wheel of a rented Kijang with Harto, ready to chauffer me around Yogyakarta.

"I have friends selling garden pots, dear Lara. Second-hand but still very good," he beamed.

With Wanto's confident driving skills, we soon found ourselves on the outskirts of Yogyakarta in what appeared to be a ceramics graveyard. Wanto, sporting his usual charisma, struck up a conversation with the caretakers and before long the boot of the Kijang was being filled with pots destined for the house in Bausasran.

When Wanto told me how much he would need to give the caretakers my mouth gaped.

"Are you sure it's enough, Harto? Can I give a small tip?"

"A tip is not necessary, Lara. Be careful with your money."

"Just a small one, Pang. And on the way back let's treat Wanto to his favourite goat satay?"

"Ya, Juragan. That is a good idea. He will be happy."

"I'm not Juragan, Pang."

Wanto bumped our heavy load back out on to the road. We were carting enough ceramic urns to open a small shop, all for the equivalent of twenty-five Australian dollars.

My third wish was for a Toyota Kijang and for Harto to be its licenced driver.

After months of rainy-season motorbike rides to school they lost some of their romance and besides that the wet weather made my hair frizzy. Mine are not the silky locks that cascade down like the hair in Sunsilk shampoo commercials; not the glossy kind that can survive the sweaty-sponge innards of a tropical helmet. Mine is not the kind of hair most Indonesian women are so blessed to have. My hair is full of unruly waves that like to set themselves into a helmet's shape or plait themselves together in the wind.

One drizzly morning I suggested it might be time for Harto to summon Wanto for my third wish. This resulted in a shiny and reliable second-hand sea green Kijang–not as modern as Pak Sungkar's but not yet a collectable like Lundy's. This iconic family wagon didn't appear in a puff of smoke. Its exhaust pipe was still in perfect condition.

Wanto found the Kijang while scanning the 'for sale' items on a public noticeboard and soon contacted Harto. Like a miracle it turned out that a middle-aged couple were selling their year 2000 Krista model, Toyota Kijang, and there were very few miles on the odometer. The husband said it had spent most of its time in their garage; that they only drove to church and back. Well, that's what Wanto told Harto, and that's what Harto told me. He made me laugh because it sounded just like the 'one lady owner to church and back' spiel that Australian used-car dealers tell prospective buyers.

But when I met the couple, I realised they had not been stretching the truth at all. They were Christians from the Presbyterian

Church of Korea working as missionaries in Indonesia. Their posting was coming to an end and they were returning to Seoul.

At Wanto's request they had driven the Kijang to the house in Bausasran for me to have a first-hand look.

They spoke softly with impeccable Indonesian grammar; prefixes and suffixes in all the right places. Sensing I was embarrassed to use mine they thoughtfully switched to English. I found their proficiency in two foreign languages impressive and their manners exceptionally polite. Their style and their ash-black hair, sprinkled with strands of white, placed them in their late fifties but their skin was as flawless as if new born.

I wondered how successful they had been with conversions in a Muslim majority nation. It struck me as a losing game. Perhaps the story of David and Goliath had filled them with high hopes. Whatever the case I declined a sweet invitation to pray together at their home. I would have felt like a fish out of water.

Undeterred and still smiling they invited me to climb in and test the comfort of the passenger seat. I checked the glove box and dashboard gadgets then under the front seats. As I fumbled around trying to adjust the seat position, I felt a heavy metal object underneath and fished out an old-fashioned red steering lock. The lock was a replica of the one my father had always hooked around the clutch of our family station wagon. At once I felt my father's spirit materialise in the present. No matter whether we believe in God or not this was surely evidence of higher forces at play.

Harto's confidence beamed when I told him the story about my father and the steering lock. He became a stickler for using it, out of respect for my father and because we both loved the Kijang. Neither of us wanted to see it stolen.

Whether Wanto materialised my wish for a Kijang; or it was just a coincidence; or was sent by my father from another realm, or whether these forces had combined, the sea-green Kijang felt special. If I hadn't wished for it, I would never have known about the post WWII wave of Korean missionaries sent to spread the Christian word in Indonesia and other Islamic countries. I was as surprised as Aladdin must have been when he first saw the genie.

The fulfilment of my third wish instantly upgraded us on the roads of Yogyakarta. Harto became the Kijang's competent driver. The days of checking the sky for threatening rain clouds were over, as were the days of plastic ponchos and wet shoes. From the day the Toyota Kijang came into our possession, Harto drove me to the language school and back. I felt like Cinderella in the pumpkin carriage on the way to the ball.

When I called Amar to let him know the good news, he told me the Krista was the best model Kijang Toyota had ever made.

"Harto will love driving it," he said, and so he did. But he still rode the old black Honda motorbike when it was more convenient, and the sun was shining.

40

On the occasional evenings when Harto was running late to pick me up from school, I would pass the time sitting with the security guard. I found it relaxing to speak in Indonesian with someone who overlooked my poor grammar and often puzzling pronunciation.

"Please, please Miss Lara. Wait here for Pak Harto. Perhaps the road is stuck tonight. Please, just sit here," he would insist.

"Thank you, Pak Bagong. You are very kind."

Apart from short exchanges with Galuh and Aji, and a kind of Indoglish with Harto, opportunities to improve in the language were rarely presented. My days at school were crammed with teaching three different levels of English, using the direct method that the school curriculum decreed worked best. The direct method meant that only the target language was to be used. Translation into the learner's mother tongue was discouraged.

As with many theories the direct method of teaching English doesn't always work. This fact was well demonstrated by a class of nine-year-olds one afternoon after dutifully practicing the four adverbs of frequency I had written on the whiteboard:

Always
Sometimes
Rarely
Never

All the little ones with their questionnaires and their pink and blue sparkle pens were mingling with each other, asking all the right multiple-choice questions:

How often do you eat noodles?
How often do you brush your teeth?
How often do you go to the cinema?
How often do you ride a bicycle?

Their confident answers assured me they had grasped the concept. Sometimes, always, rarely, and sometimes never. Wonderful! Success! Until…they come in a huddle to my desk with their notepads to get their 'good job' stickers and they look up with their big earnest eyes and ask:

"Miss Lara, what is always? What is rarely? What is never?"

"Okay, let me show you quickly on the whiteboard. Let's play the memory game." I say, springing into action. "Let's make doubly sure you understand. Everyone ready? Come on boys. Come and watch the disappearing words."

I check the corridor is clear of parents and that Harold, the Director of Studies, is still tuned to the BBC news in his office next door. Then I gather the children in a conspiracy circle and write a second list on the whiteboard:

Always – *selalu*
Sometimes – *kadang-kadang*
Rarely – *jarang*
Never – *tidak pernah.*

The little girls with their big eyes and small notebooks break into surprised smiles of comprehension. The penny has dropped. Meanwhile the little boys continue their bullfight on the carpet.

After that I don't stick to the direct method religiously. It saves a lot of time and confusion and makes no difference to the end result. Harold is none the wiser but the children are–especially the girls.

Little ones are natural teachers. Mine had no qualms about correcting my pronunciation. And not just with the Indonesian words I sometimes used. They liked to correct my English pronunciation too, so it would sound like theirs. One day I told them if they were too noisy, they would have to do twenty push-ups!

"You mean puuusap Miss Lara," said a chorus of little girls, one of whom then marched over to the white board and wrote PUSAP diagonally in huge letters with a red felt marker. Turning to face me, she replaced the cap with her knee-to-a-grasshopper height and folded her arms with a sense of self-righteous satisfaction.

"Okay, Febri, thank you for the correction. Now everyone, show me how to do twenty PUSAP please!" I say to keep an upper hand.

"And then we'll do alphabet aerobics. You can take turns. Miss Lara will sit at the desk and judge the most creative action. And then we'll see who can stare at this dot on the whiteboard for the longest. Without blinking. Or talking. The winner can sing 'The Good Ship Lollipop' song in front of the class!"

Those raucous little kids couldn't help but make my days bright. They were like spoonfuls of sherbet, mixed with spice. Sometimes pronunciation is better left the way it naturally comes out.

"How do you know the second verse of the lollipop song? I only taught you the first verse!" I ask, dropping my jaw in surprise after the winner has entertained the class and her mini-sized audience has gathered in a little group around my desk.

"YouTube of course, Miss Lara!" That's when I realised the time had come to update my silver Nokia to a Blackberry.

The kids at the English school were not kampung kids like Galuh's girls, Rani and Ninik. Though later they would both go to university on scholarships. These were kids with the privilege of owning fancy mobile phones. Most were dropped off by drivers in cars that were just as flash. Their parents were doctors and dentists and lawyers. Indonesia is a country of wealth and poverty. Whether you will be born into a charmed life or one where you will scratch and scrape enough to live is a lottery.

The teenagers I taught slumped in their chairs as teenagers have a way of doing all over the world and having or feigning a complete disinterest in school. A class of teenagers can sometimes look like fifteen bottles of lethargy with attitude.

"Come on everyone! Where's your spirit? Did you leave your energy under the bed this morning?"

Just grumpy looks, except for Nicholas who was always alert, always helpful and already fluent in English. Nicholas was the type of student who saves teachers of teenagers from despair.

"Come on everyone! Let's play celebrity chairs. Nadya, you can be first (pause) Okay so, no questions from any of you?"

"Yes Miss Lara, I have a question for Nadya."

"Thank you, Nicholas. Please, go ahead." Nicholas planned to be a pilot.

"Nadya, what job would you like to do in the future?" he asks.

"I will be scientist like Professor Einstein" says Nadya, taking a while to stew her answer first.

And so, it goes on for eighty slow minutes. This teeth-pulling for a single response until my jaw aches from smiling encouragement and my crows-feet have become more permanent.

Despite them testing my patience to the far end of its elastic, I refuse to give up on them. I know this awkward phase will eventually pass. A science magazine I once read said the larger teenage brain that wants to defy authority will settle into its mature and more responsible adult size around the age of twenty-one.

All the English teachers suffered through those teenage classes and tried to trade them. But we all looked forward to the students who came to the two classes after Maghrib. They were from all the universities around Yogyakarta, and needing to improve their English for the papers they were required to write. They always paid attention. And they had their stories, which I loved them to tell and later write.

One night an older male student walked into my classroom and sat at the back. His tight curly hair, which was cut short, had a distinctive grey streak in the front. His features a little different from the mainly Javanese faces of the students I taught. Perhaps he is from West Timor or Maluku, I wondered, or somewhere in the Nusantara stretch of Islands. I would find out soon enough, I thought, as I put my bag on the teacher's desk. This was the first lesson of an upper-intermediate course so introductions would be coming up next.

"Hello everyone, welcome to my classroom. My name is Miss Lara," I introduced myself and began to write on the whiteboard, reciting the words as I went:

> Miss Lara.
>
> I'm from Brisbane, Australia.
>
> My favourite colour is green.
>
> My favourite creature is a seahorse. A seahorse is magical and mysterious.
>
> My favourite place is Yogyakarta.

And with the last one, I turn to wink because most of the students would say the same.

"Now, let's throw this yellow ball around the room. When you catch it, please introduce yourself and tell us about you." I tossed the ball towards a confident looking girl wearing a head scarf. She began:

My name is Nindia Putri Ayu.
You can call me, Ayu.
I am from Bandung, West Java.
I study at UIN University
My favourite animal is cat. Cat is soft and mysterious.

And that's how a yellow ball with a smiley-face motif rolled through the air helping a nervous class relax and laugh and become more familiar. Nindia threw the ball to a handsome boy on the other side of the room, giggling:

My name is Wisnu Mahendra Jaya Putra.
You can call me Wisnu.
My favourite animal is dog. Dog is friendly and loyal.
I study at Gajah Mada University.
My favourite place to visit is Prambanan Temple.

"Aah, that's one of my favourite places, too! By the way good catch! Now throw the ball to another classmate?"

Hello everyone, my name is Franciskus Tukan.
I'm from Mataloko in Flores.
My favourite colour is red.
My favourite creature is the dragon because dragons can live in two worlds. They're strong and adaptable. Some experts say that Komodo dragons are the last dinosaurs. They originally came from Australia.

Even before he answers the last question, I have a feeling this class will be interesting. His next answer confirms it.

My favourite place is Botswana. I'm here in Yogyakarta for three years. I will study at Sanata Dharma University to become an English teacher.

"We're very lucky to have you join our class Franciskus. I hope we will hear more about Botswana." Although he never mentions he's a missionary priest, he has a certain presence, and his last answer makes the whole class curious. There are twenty-three classes left of the course. In them, we will learn a few things about his time in Botswana and about his life at Mataloko Catholic Seminary in Flores.

41

When I return to my desk in the teacher's room after that first lesson there's a buzz.

"Lara, we heard you have a Catholic priest in your class," says Emma cheekily.

"Oh, I wondered that, but he wasn't wearing a priest's collar."

"Ask him next time," says everyone in the room.

"I'm not going to ask him that! He seems very sweet and a bit shy. And why all this gossip, don't you have lessons to plan," I remind, attempting to change the subject.

"We just think he looks cute, that's all," says Emma on everyone's behalf.

"Show some respect, freaks," chides Carl. "I met Father Franciskus downstairs earlier. He seems like a lovely man. And don't forget I'm an ordained minister myself, though not the celibate kind," he adds, with a mischievous blue eye surveying the room through a silver-rimmed monocle—his latest acquisition.

"Oh, that's right, Carl. What's the name of your church again," I call across from my desk.

Carl was as flamboyant as Oscar Wilde but he adored women–especially the single mother who had raised him in Somerset, England and his Indonesian wife, Sani, with her looks and style reminiscent of Yoko Ono. She and Carl made a stunning couple. Carl had spent a few years in San Francisco before they met and that's how he came to be ordained as a minister of the Universal Church of Light—a sort of hippie, non-denominational church, from what I gathered.

"What are you teaching tonight?" I sing across the room to Emma, who, with her iridescent blue eyes and flaming red hair, is busily writing up a set of flash cards.

"Speed dating and adjectives to describe your perfect match. Hope the students have better luck than me," she mutters.

"Why are you saying that, Emma? You and Rafi seem so happy together."

"Past tense, Lara. He told me yesterday he wanted to bring a second wife home. I told him no way! Then he accused me of being too American. Maybe he forgot I'm from Minnesota."

"Oh, I'm so sorry to hear that, Emma."

"Thanks, Lara, I need to look for a lawyer." And so, she did.

Over the next few months Emma negotiated her divorce through an Islamic Court, adding a whole new set of law-related vocabulary to her already fluent Indonesian. Thanks to a background in fine arts, and blessed with natural talent, she was able to make and sell feather jewellery on the side. It kept her sane and helped cover the legal costs as she continued to teach on a small salary and juggle her two curly-headed boys.

"Where's Tina by the way? I haven't seen her all day," I ask, noticing her empty desk beside Emma.

Tina was a young woman from Melbourne, a blue-eyed blond with a Bachelor degree in Asian Studies and a no-nonsense attitude. She was born with leadership skills but never looked for glory. These assets came in handy for Harold, our British Director of Studies. He, and we, relied on Tina's organisational skills, and her natural affinity with microphones. No one else but Tina could get a gaggle of students into line from the front of a school excursion bus.

"She's downstairs in Harold's office organising the roster for the spelling bee on Saturday. He doesn't have time now that he has a new baby at home," quips Carl.

"How tiring to start a new family at his age," I say, thinking out loud, though Harold could pass for fifty.

"He's turning sixty-five this year; old enough to qualify for the British pension," shoots back Carl from his desk, where he's sketching figures for the younger students to clothe and colour.

"Speaking of age, Amar will be turning twenty-eight soon. It feels like yesterday he was just a baby. He and Alin have set their wedding date for July. Alin's mother and I are having matching kebaya made in Jakarta."

"You don't look old enough to have son that age," comforts Hannah, as she fishes for ideas in the filing cabinet drawers.

"Thanks Hannah, you're worth a few gold star stickers. What are you teaching tonight?"

"I'm doing a lesson on stereotypes and different cultures. Has anyone seen the beach ball globe of the world? I need it for a game."

Hannah, with her Princess Diana legs and her shy smile would always joke that her Midlands British accent was the least posh in the room, though her manners were the most polite. She embodied kindness, often leaving thoughtful gifts on my desk. Sometimes caramel toffees her mother would send from England.

"Emma, I could ask Iwan to order a bottle of gin or vodka for you," she sings out thoughtfully. Iwan, Hannah's Javanese husband ran a trendy bistro in Jalan Sosrowijayan.

"How is the gorgeous, Iwan," asks Jacinta throwing Hannah the globe ball.

"As good as gold, Jacinta," she smiles shyly.

"Aah, the gorgeous man list is beginning to outnumber the bad apples," notes Nurani, our Indonesian head teacher who understands

English grammar better than a native speaker and has a very individual sense of style and humour.

Nurani would often mix and match odd items of clothing making the world a brighter place. Sometimes a peasant skirt with a denim shirt, blue nail polish and a pair of ankle boots with rainbow-coloured socks. She wore a headband with bunny ears for teaching all the little ones who ran up the corridors to hug her legs when they arrived for lessons.

I'm sure her unconventional spirit helped when she went against her Catholic family's wishes and married the musician and artful chef she fell in love with at university—a devout Muslim. Still, she made both families proud when, as part of a dance troupe, she performed in front of Megawati Sukarno Putri, Indonesia's fifth president, daughter of the first.

"Hey, what about Roger," jokes Jacinta from her neat desk beside the door, "he's not a bad guy."

Jacinta, all of twenty-one and with a model's face and figure that made everyone look twice, had come for a year's break in between finishing a Bachelor of Asian Studies, and dedicating herself to writing a doctoral thesis on Indonesia and Australia's relationship in regard to asylum seekers. Once, to my envy, she interviewed Marty Natalegawa, who was at the time, Indonesia's cool-cat foreign minister.

"Thank you, Jacinta, yeah, what about me," asks Roger, with his Cockney accent.

"There's a bad apple in every bunch, but the rest are tasty."

"You're not a bad apple, Roger," says Emma teasing.

"No, he's a delicious fruit salad," says Jacinta, laughing. And with that we all crack up because Roger only ever ate fruit.

Before Roger taught English, he was picking bodies out of wells in Haiti. That was after he came to Yogyakarta as a relief worker in the aftermath of the 2006 earthquake and met his wife, Desi. After two major disasters he was suffering post-traumatic stress and needed a change of scene. He turned up at the school one day looking for alternative work. Harold couldn't turn him away. When Harold mentioned that Roger had blue eyes like Daniel Craig from the James Bond movies, neither could we.

"Don't worry Harold, leave him with us," said the girls. We took Roger under our wings and gave him a crash course in verb tenses and how to teach idioms. He took to teaching like a duck to water.

"Thanks for the offer of alcohol, Hannah," says Emma "but imported gin would cost a month of wages."

"We can all contribute," Nurani suggests, "that's the Indonesian way."

"You mean *chip in*," says Jacinta, throwing in a phrasal verb.

As we joked around in the teachers' room that night, in our usual fashion, I was completely unaware that when Father Franciskus walked into my classroom that night, he'd walked into my life and would become a treasured friend. I didn't know that three years later I would be editing his bachelor thesis and a decade on, while he was in Chicago furthering his English studies, I would help with his assignments and spend hours on the phone hearing about his experiences in all the big cities of America. I could never have imagined that in the future he would become my confidante; listen to my confessions, see my tears and be my strength.

And I could never have imagined that all this would take place on the small video screen of a smart-phone; the device that would supersede the Blackberry I hadn't even bought yet!

That night as I walked down the corridor to my last class, I still had my faithful old silver Nokia tucked into the side pocket of my teacher's tote bag, along with a sense of security that Harto was only a text message away, or twenty minutes' drive in a Toyota Kijang.

42

Indonesians are early risers. Most are up by dawn. Best to get the chores and cooking done before the damp blanket of heat descends for the day. Devout Muslims get up even earlier with Sholat Subuh, the first call to prayer, when Arabic chants crackle out from loudspeakers, piercing the morning stillness well before sunrise. But I still struggle to wake up.

Today as I linger in bed planning lessons in my head, the swishing, sweeping sound of Aji's broom is drowned out by the noisy thoroughfare our street becomes for parents who pillion their children to a nearby school.

Rolling over I throw a blind arm out for Harto but am met instead with an empty flat-sheet space. My disappointment melts into the sunlight filtering through the shutters as I remember our conversation the night before at Superindo.

"The fruit is too expensive in the supermarket, Lara. I will go to Pasar Beringharjo market in the morning."

No doubt Harto will have already joined the throng at the local market. It's a good enough incentive to get up and make my way to the bathroom for a *mandi*.

The unwelcome march of middle age demands an extra effort to crawl out of bed, although I must admit I've never been a morning person. I envy people who are, and wonder if they're born or made and if there's still any hope for me to change. My grandmother was always up with the birds, all domestic duties done, cushions plumped to perfection and a day's dishes cooked before breakfast. A proud descendent of Chinese stock, and a stickler for self-discipline.

Mixed with Irish blood, my mother railed against a structured life. She was always up till the midnight hours surrounded by fabrics and the haberdashery of her creations, imagining more romance in a mirror that reflected dreams in the shape or drape of a newly pinned pattern. She found more promise in a new dress than anything a polished home could provide. Caught at a crossroads between the two I try to balance both.

Though they still drop into my thoughts neither is here to help me now or nudge me out of bed. But at least I know I can count on a few ladles of cool water from our traditional mandi to kickstart the day. A traditional old house comes with a traditional bathroom– summoning my inherited romantic side. A brisk fountain of youth in a ceramic tiled tub!

The scent of jasmine soap fills the bathroom air, and as the water douses my fatigue, my thoughts wander to one of my four sisters who runs a country bed and breakfast. She emailed recently to say that she and her neighbours were anxiously waiting out fire season. She said the river that runs behind her property had all but dried up. She used to love swimming in it but now she can walk right across its dusty pebbled bed. She can't remember the last time it rained.

This distant reverie peters out as I wrap my wet hair in a towel, tie on a sarong and step out of the watery bathroom.

Harto is back from the markets; his deft hand responsible for the plates of fruit on the kitchen table, piled high with slices of glossy mango and slivered red papaya.

While I'm spooning fat dollops of yoghurt onto fruit, Galuh arrives, the sound of her rusty old bicycle hitting the concrete driveway signals to Harto her late morning arrival.

"Galuh is lazy. She is late again as usual," he tuts. But I'm not sure he's right. because the rattle of her bicycle is always followed by the rustle of plastic shopping bags. She has obviously been to the markets early as she is loaded up with fresh produce for the day's cooking. Tahu and tempeh, the two much loved staples of the Indonesian diet lead a procession out of the plastic shopping bags and onto the low tiled bench. Snake beans follow, then leafy greens, carrots, cauliflower, garlic, ginger, shaved coconut, red onions and two types of hot chilli. Galuh will have bargained them all down to a price that I would never dare. Bargaining is a birth right for Indonesians. I find it a challenge and if I am successful, it's usually compensated for with a measure of guilt in the form of a few extra rupiah much to the seller's delight and the family's amusement.

"We're going to the beach on Sunday, Galuh, would you like to come too?" I blurt out over the big teak breakfast table.

"Ya, Juragan, and how about Rani and Ninik," she calls from the kitchen.

"Yes, of course," I call back, "and Aji must come too. Harto won't mind at all," I answer, not knowing whether he will or not.

43

We wait eagerly for Sunday to roll around. By the time it does, Aji has polished the Kijang to a smiling shine that has spread to his face. Galuh arrives donning a pair of big square sunglasses transforming her into a fashion magazine model. She's loaded up with sunhats and other sun protective clothes, bags of snacks and bottled water. The girls straggle in behind her with their canvas beach bags.

We climb into the Kijang and shuffle into our positions. There are still plenty of unused miles on the clock, which we intend to make use of. The weather is clear, the sun bright, and the world, or at least this corner of it, is our oyster.

Harto takes the wheel and steers the car out onto the road and into the traffic. The girls have brought cassettes of their favourite music. Ninik hands one over to Harto. He slots it in. Their favourite Indonesian pop music crackles out from speakers in the back and they start to sing along until the air conditioning bothers them so we turn it off and weave through the streets of Yogyakarta, all windows down, heading for the southern ring road and the turn off to the South Seas.

The narrow highway sews a continuous seam through a verdant green fabric of rice paddies, set against a curtain backdrop of tall coconut palms. After an hour or so the road trails off and zigzags into a track that starts to twist and turn gently downhill. We have arrived on the outskirts of the coastal villages. Even though we've slowed down, the winding road has made Ninik feel nauseous and Galuh tells Harto to pull over quickly. "Ninik wants to throw up!"

Harto takes her instruction with no argument. As he pulls over to the side, I turn around to see the pallor of poor little Ninik's face. She's turned slightly green.

Harto and Aji amble down the road taking the opportunity to light up a clove cigarette. They've heard my speeches about the perils of passive smoking and must be afraid of inviting another one.

We wait patiently for Ninik to recover. When she does, I wave a signal to Harto. He and Aji grind out their cigarettes on the sandy tarmac road and saunter up the hill.

"Please go slowly Uncle," begs Ninik, still looking pale as she climbs back into the car and swaps her furthest back seat with Aji's middle one. Harto bumps the Kijang more gently over the next few dips and Galuh puts the fried snacks she has brought out of sight.

Finally, we arrive at our destination, Baron fishing beach, tucked away in a sandy cove. Big signs in the parking areas warn of the dangers of swimming. But I notice Nyi Roro Kidul, the south sea goddess, is not as jealous as she is in Parangtritis. She laps the shore in a gentle, tranquil manner. This clever disguise has managed to lure a few timid paddlers.

Though it's still early a big crowd has arrived. Fishermen in conical bamboo hats have already netted a catch and begun to sell what they can from the bottoms of their brightly coloured boats. Weekend tourists from all over Indonesia have arrived by the busload and some have gathered on the sand to marvel at the spoils. We can hear them haggling excitedly over prices.

Stalls in the parking area have souvenirs for sale, adding to a busy market day mood. Sellers strung with wares wander up and down the beach offering variations of the same: beach hats, umbrellas, shells and beads. The day is alive and full of sunshine and the sky a beautiful turquoise blue. Cotton wool clouds reflect themselves in a glass-mirror of sea. Thankfully the ocean breeze has brought the colour back to Ninik's cheeks and she's laughing as she attempts to take funny photos of Rani and Aji with my pocket camera.

Galuh relaxes onto a woven beach mat and watches Rani and Ninik through her fashion model sunglasses with a surf lifesaver's alertness, as they make their way to the water. They paddle in the shallows searching for shrimp and shells. She calls out from under her big brimmed hat,

"Don't go too far into the waves," and the universal mother's warning, "*Hati-hati!*" Be careful.

They've rubbed sunscreen all over their faces and apart from rolled up jeans their limbs are well covered. Galuh has spare clothes at the ready should they happen to need them. She's afraid the sun might darken their skin, and hers. This is a country of skin whitening creams and billboard commercials about them. There are no bikinis on this beach. Everyone swims fully dressed.

My tanning days are long over and I'm fully covered up too. A small troupe of giggling teenage girls approach and ask if they can have their photo taken with me. They need photos of foreigners for a school project, they persist.

'Yes, of course,' I say, grinning up at a group of head-scarved faces set against the clear sky. As quick as a Polaroid can develop a photo, they all pull out their mobile phone cameras and I get my Andy Warhol fifteen minutes of fame, happily answering all the interview question:

"Which country are you from, Miss?"
"What is your job?"
"What is your favourite place in Yogyakarta?"
"Do you have children, Miss?"

To this, I answer that I have one son and that even though he is Australian, he has an Indonesian name.

"I'll show you" I smile, and write AMAR in the sand with my finger from right to left. The girls read as I draw, gaping as his hidden name is revealed. RAMA, they clap and chatter excitedly.

"Aah…you are very clever to see that his name is a mirror for the hero of the Ramayana story. His name was chosen to reflect the same noble qualities; to remind him to live a virtuous life and do good deeds."

"And become rich, Miss, like a king."

"Inshallah," I smile. "God willing."

I show them a photo of Amar looking like a male model with his jade green eyes, and his blond-tipped hair and his builder muscles.

"I wish I can be his girlfriend, Miss," sighs one, with her hand pressed to her heart.

"I'm afraid you're a little too late. He has already found Sinta."

And with that they huddle off in their headscarves, laughing as they compare their loot of photos. Their energy lights the day even more brightly and I'm happy to oblige. After all, their country has opened its arms to me.

Galuh and I settle back on the sand again, pulling the brims of our sunhats down. Harto strolls over to a stall where a woman in ragged clothes is selling young coconuts. We watch while he picks and chooses. At last, he spots the biggest, and bargains for the best price. He pulls his wallet from his back pocket and pays with a small rupiah note. She tucks it into the bodice of her faded kebaya then deftly slices the top off the large coconut with her rusty machete and trims the edges.

Aji wanders down to test the water. He wades out a little further past the girls who are dipping their feet in the shallows. Suddenly he loses his footing on the slippery stones underfoot and turns back to move in closer. Like Harto, he hasn't learned to swim. Galuh and I are watching with our lifeguard eyes when Rani and Ninik begin to splash him. A water fight breaks out and shrieks of laughter. Before long all three are soaked and their clothes stuck. Aji's loose T-shirt is stretched and sagging. The pockets of his army shorts are heavy with sand and water. He still has the strap of liquorice black hair but soon it will be gone. Cut short and spiked with gel.

Eventually, the three flop out of the water and drip back to where Galuh and I have spread out picnic boxes of *nasi gudeg*, Yogyakarta's most famous dish. The dish consists of sweet marinated jackfruit mixed with fresh grated coconut, chickens' feet, hard-boiled eggs and Harto's favourite part, beef skin that looks like an orange-soaked sponge. These delicacies are naturally served with rice.

Harto eats at a snail's pace, wary of small bitumen stones that find their way into threshed rice left out to dry on roadsides. He's broken two back teeth on stones. They make me cautious too.

After lunch we climb up to the cliff top. Galuh and I make our way up together followed by Rani, Ninik and Aji. Harto follows along a short distance behind. We take up positions in a gazebo that looks out over the rugged coastline and breathe in the spectacular views, along with the salty sea air. Rani and Ninik, with their hair blowing into their mouths and faces, decide in which direction Australia sits. I wave a big hello and blow kisses that the wind carries off. It makes them giggle; then Galuh mentions she wants to buy some tropical fish before we leave. The wind is gusty so we head back down and over the sand to a makeshift aquarium made from big plastic sheets.

Galuh and the girls point out the colourful fish they want to buy. The seller scoops them up and plops them into a plastic bag filled with seawater.

On the way back to the car, Harto stops at a market stall. To my surprise he buys a bamboo fishing hat the size of an umbrella. His smile, as he wobbles it on his head, matches the size of this bigger than usual model.

"Wonderful, Pang, it's big enough to be a shelter for us if Bausasran ever falls down," I joke, laughing at the spectacle of it all.

"This is *seni*," he sings out, flashing another smile. "This is art!"

We take turns to wash our sandy feet with buckets of fresh water in the parking area and then pile into the car, our energy spent. Soon Aji, Galuh and the girls nod off. I glance across at Harto. His eyes are focused on the road—military style. The old Kijang doesn't miss a beat and soon enough we're back home and it's his turn to take a nap.

Indonesians have mastered the art of napping in the afternoon and Harto is no exception. Within minutes he is sprawled out and dozing on the Persian carpet in the living room under the tinkling chandelier. As I watch Galuh and the girls dawdle out through the garage with the wobbling bag of tropical fish I'm brimming with happiness over the whole day.

During our days in Bausasran, we took many trips to the southern beaches in the sea-green Kijang, either with the whole family, or just the two of us. Sometimes we would take Saraswati and her mother Mbah Salim and Bhima to the coastal village of Wonosari to visit relatives. And we always took friends and family who came to visit.

44

Among the visitors who came to stay at the house in Bausasran was an older American friend called Sheena; my role model of an independent woman. Her accounts of a free-range childhood spent roaming the woods of upstate New York with a younger brother must have planted little seeds of adventure in her blood.

Every so often she would chug the five hours from Gubeng Station in Surabaya on the Sanjaka train, to stay for a weekend, hauling a canvas duffle bag full of books. Despite her busy work schedule, she'd have managed to read them all at night tucked up in her little house in Taman Pinang, a short pedicab ride away from the cottage where I had lived with Harto. The books would be exchanged at the second-hand bookstore behind the famous backpacker street of Jalan Sosrowijayan.

Both Harto and I treasured the times when the Sanjaka diesel train would come roaring along the railway line from the east with Sheena on board. We'd wait eagerly for the doors of her carriage to spring open and deposit her neatly onto one of the seven platforms that make up Tugu Station–still set in the nutmeg and cinnamon colours of a colonial-era time warp.

With her canvas bags in tow, Sheena would step down from her carriage, noting on the station clock with a wry smile how the Sanjaka, in complete disregard for Indonesian rubber time, was right on schedule.

Like a soldier on official duty, Harto would retrieve her bags, lifting and weaving them through the chattering crowd, as he led us to the proudly polished sea-green Kijang–brim-full of petrol and ready to take Sheena to all the places in Yogyakarta she would surely like to visit.

I suspect Sheena was in her late sixties at the time, and for all the world knew she was just another senior citizen, but to me she was exceptional. She had once travelled for five hours to the Togean Islands, sitting on the wooden deck of a freighter because the public ferry was broken. She had been sorry to see the poor state of the coral, reporting that the snorkelling wasn't that good. She had sailed to the Banda Islands and tasted the nutmeg and other famous spices. And travelled on muddy roads from Palu, in central Sulawesi, to Lore Linda in the north to see the wildlife. She had ticked Toraja, South Sulawesi, with its ancient burial rites, off her list of desires. She carried little more than a Lonely Planet guidebook, a bi-lingual dictionary, and a few essential Indonesian words under her belt.

We had first met in the foyer of the language school in Sidoarjo one morning before the students arrived for classes. Harto and I had walked the short distance to introduce ourselves. We were so happy that day. I'd just signed a yearlong rental contract with the owner of the cottage in exchange for one thousand Australian dollars. And we had bought some furniture: a bed, a small fridge and a gas burner.

Though I was still nervous about starting a teaching career, my good mood and my fashion background had seen me flaunting a summery skirt in a floral print, teamed with a fuchsia-coloured shirt and bright matching lipstick.

In complete contrast Sheena was wearing a self-styled uniform of sensible baggy trousers and a pale blue polo shirt. Her grey hair was cropped short and she wore bifocal glasses. Unlike me she didn't wear any make up. On her hands I noticed two artistic silver rings set with large coloured stones that seem to speak of maps and travel.

Sheena had a relaxed demeanour and the friendliest smile I'd ever seen. Her smile said, "I'm happy to see you. I'm gonna take you right now to your desk in the teachers' room, before you change your mind." Harto excused himself, reversing out the front door with his own smile, saying he would pass the time with Pak Agus the school driver we had met at the airport.

The younger American director of studies I had expected to meet that day was nowhere to be seen. The talkative one who had quizzed me about modal verbs when we spoke on the phone. The one who had rattled off a list of strict rules for each day of the week stating firmly that Bahasa Indonesia was not to be used at any time, within the walls of the two-story school building, then talked about gold star performance charts and sticker rewards with as much vigour. She'd had rules for rules.

During my years in the fashion industry there had been one or two young women with the same controlling drive. I knew how overbearing they could be. My relief to have escaped came beaming out in a smile that accompanied the words, "So nice to meet you, Sheena. See you on Monday! I can't wait to start!"

Sheena wasn't a big talker like the stereotypical American, and she didn't talk as much as me. But then she wasn't one of five sisters, daughters of a Scorpio mother, who sometimes liked to sing soprano. She spoke little but she spoke a lot between the lines. All she ever said about her former husband was that he was Italian-American, and that's how she got the surname that didn't match her clear blue eyes.

She had been married and divorced once and had two grown-up boys. Both in their forties. One married and one single. Both athletic. One liked kayaking. She joked, saying it surprised her how well they turned out despite her mothering skills; not cooking much and too much time with her head down studying science books. Then one day she had a car accident, when she wasn't concentrating on the road. The boys got off with light injuries. Hers were critical.

Whether this caused the breakdown of her marriage I don't know but whatever the case Sheena had moved on from her separation so much better than I had. Despite the many joys this new life was bringing me, my heart was still limping along in a quagmire as slippery as Lapindo mudflow. But I never mentioned it. I dared not show such shoddy signs of weakness to this new heroine of mine.

While Sheena and I both lived in the housing estate of Taman Pinang we became good friends. Often, we'd share taxis into Surabaya to pick up groceries we weren't able to get in Sidoarjo. Sheena would stock up on plain yoghurt to feed her osteoporosis, and calcium tablets if the import price wasn't too high. On the odd occasion we'd buy Italian wine and French Camembert at the upmarket Sogo department store.

Most days Sheena swam laps at the local swimming pool. One morning I joined her. Sheena swam twenty laps in slow and steady strokes to my one. Not that I couldn't swim, it was just that I never got the breathing technique right. But I preferred to keep my mornings for preparing lessons at home, rather than in the cacophony of the teachers' room. A well-structured lesson plan was as important to me as a good pattern design. I envied teachers who could wing lessons straight off the cuff. Sheena herself could have calmly taught a class blindfolded with her hands tied behind her back and performed a few Houdini tricks at the same time.

"You'll be able to do that some day, Lara," Sheena would say with her big smile. But years later I still planned lessons in detail.

Once, when Harto was in Yogyakarta, we booked a weekend at the Majahpahit in Surabaya; the grand hotel where the Dutch flag was pulled down in the battle for independence. That weekend I was privileged to hear three of Sheena's life stories.

The first two stories were of loss and courage told in the matter-of-fact style that belonged only to her. The third story was lighter and full of surprises–an adventure story, where Sheena herself became my heroine. We had just enjoyed a rare meal of Australian lamb chops with mashed potato, steamed broccoli and real butter, in the fancy hotel restaurant, when the stories surfaced.

"My mother was a nurse," she began, telling me that her mother had been asthmatic and ill for some time before she passed away. She said her mother had suffered from lung cancer and not enough pain relief. She suspected her mother had drawn on her nursing knowledge to hasten the inevitable with a larger dose of pills than the doctor had prescribed. She couldn't be sure. But she'd always wondered.

The look in Sheena's eyes, behind her green framed glasses, was so clouded in that moment I was lost for words. To this day I regret not having asked her more about it. Did she remember the last words they shared? Did her suspicions influence the way she lived now? How did she feel about her mother? In that situation would she do the same?

I knew that Sheena didn't believe in an almighty God. She believed the human race created God. At university she'd studied science. For Sheena any so-called evidence of God could be argued out of existence. She preferred travel guides over hymn books, catechisms or the holy bible.

"There was a time when I couldn't eat lamb chops," she had said, moving on to her second story. After the car accident all her teeth were extracted and her jaw wired shut. For eight months she lay in a hospital bed. For the first few weeks she was fed through a tube until she was able to suck pureed food through a plastic straw. She said the one positive side of her jaw being wired shut was that she couldn't drag on cigarettes. She never smoked again.

After this long confinement she decided never to stay in just one place again. And after so long in hospital her home felt like a strange empty place. Perhaps her husband found someone who could fine-dine on scaloppini by candlelight. I should have asked more about that and about her boys, but Sheena was a private person.

Since then, she had gained a Masters' degree in Hydrology and lived in Botswana and the Philippines working for the Peace Corps on better irrigation systems for growing crops.

"I sold my house in the States to travel. Put the cash into savings bonds. Then the market crashed and most of it disappeared," she told me. "Not that I was ever rich. I'll have to keep working for a while."

"Rich doesn't always mean fruitful, Sheena."

"Wise words Lara. I'd say my life has been as fruitful as the strawberries and ice cream on the table," she said, her dry humour and the bowls of dessert bringing smiles back to our faces.

The third story Sheena told was about her travels through Indonesia. When she first arrived to teach English, she had set herself the goal of visiting as many islands as she could. She liked to tick them off in her Lonely Planet guidebook. She had even hitched a ride in a small motorboat out to Anak Krakatoa—the offspring of the once fiery Krakatoa that blew itself to smithereens in 1883.

Sheena understood a lot more Indonesian than she spoke. On one of her more remote travel destinations, she recognised three words used to describe her, spoken into a telephone by the receptionist of the only hotel around. She hadn't bothered to book a room assuming the place would be deserted. Instead, there were busloads of Indonesian tourists. She said the young woman was so concerned about the lack of accommodation she asked her family to help. That's when Sheena heard the worried words come out:

"Ibu! Bule! Sendiri!" Woman! White! Alone!

"That's a great story, Sheena, but I think we should add *mandiri*, for independent," I said laughing. "The staff would have been surprised to see you travelling alone. Indonesia is such a group culture! I'm amazed, too, because I've never been intrepid enough to travel to unknown places alone."

In 2012, when Sheena eventually packed up her house to leave Indonesia with a plan to retire in Panama, she put two things she couldn't carry into a cardboard box and had them freight-trained to me. I knew they were some of her treasured things because I'd heard the stories. There was a woven bowl made by the women of Botswana, and a carved *cendrahwasih* bird that she had once carried back from Bali in her cabin luggage. She couldn't resist its tail, all sanded and painted in splendid chalky colours.

"It might not be to your taste, Lara, but I know you'll look after it for me," she wrote in a note.

I put the bird in pride of place on the lounge room credenza, where it sat happily, until one morning when I bumped its elaborate tail while rounding the corner to the bedroom in a hurry. It crashed onto the tiled floor and shattered. I was horrified! Harto gathered up the pieces and spent every spare minute he could over the next few weeks cross-legged on the Persian carpet surrounded by the puzzle pieces of it. All the carving skills he had learned from his father as a child came back, and they were needed, because that carved bird of paradise had become a manifestation of Sheena to us.

Sheena's bones were as fragile as that wooden bird, but her inner strength was steel. She was the tourist guide in her own life. On one of her visits to Bausasran she bought some handmade toys from a street vendor: a bicycle and a *becak* pedicab. They were replicas with as much detail as the life-sized ones. Those she managed to squeeze into her luggage and, until she adjusted to her life in Panama, I would send her favourite Robusta coffee.

45

Buying odd things from street vendors was something both Sheena and I enjoyed on her visits. Peddlers would often push their loaded carts past the house advertising their wares with jingling bell sticks. They sold all sorts of things from handmade toys to bed-brooms, doormats, cooking pots and buckets.

Whenever we heard the jingles and the rasp of cart wheels on the road outside, we'd spy through the batik curtains that Saraswati had made, to see what was on offer.

Once I bought a whole cartful of terracotta garden pots from a crooked old man with tough-soled feet and few remaining teeth. The bucket–sized pots made a perfect row along a concrete path that bordered the back garden.

Aji strode them into the garden shed on one shoulder. Then he rode off on his shiny new Yamaha to the plant nurseries near the zoo with instructions to buy twelve leafy plants. By the time Aji left Bausasran, those plants had grown like beanstalks, all the way up the mossy concrete walls. Those were his most carefree days and some of my happiest. Aji had worked with us for about a year when I came up with the bright idea of Aji owning his own two wheels.

"Pang, I think we should help Aji to buy a motorbike to run errands," I suggested, a few months after the house painting was finished and the floor tiles brought back to a shine with coconut oil and rags and muscle–and Aji's wish to please.

"Lara, don't spoil him too much."

"Just a little step up for him, Pang, and it would be for my benefit. There might be a time when Saraswati or Bhima need you suddenly, and you can't pick me up from school," I pleaded, pulling my powers of persuasion out of the bedside table drawer along with a pen and notebook.

"How about a Yamaha, like Saraswati's red one?"

"Up to you, Lara, if you want to spend your money. But you must reduce his monthly wage to compensate."

"Please organise it for me, Pang. You are the real Juragan and we both know it," I groaned.

"Okay, Lara, I will speak to him. I will tell him you will cut his wage by one third each month. He will be happy," Harto replied, with a little smile of sarcasm from the mirror on the wall, as he plucked out his chin whiskers with my tweezers.

"He will be more than happy, since his wage is a third above the average."

Within the week, a shiny new black Yamaha 150cc motorbike makes its first appearance under the pendopo. The following week the muffler is suddenly noisy. The decibels are enough to wake the whole neighbourhood and we have to ask Aji to wheel the motorbike past the gate before he starts it. The noise of its constant comings and goings have frayed my nerves and riled Harto's. He gives Aji an angry warning, but the noise persists. Aji is as if possessed.

He begins to add accessories. Every night when I arrive home from the English school, he appears to have added a new one. He becomes obsessed with polishing the chrome and neglects the housework. Believe it or not, he actually goes out one night in a loose T-shirt and wheels the bike back through the garage wearing a tight black leather jacket, complete with silver metal zips and studs! Then, as a final touch, he adds a Playboy bunny sticker to the tank!

We are witnessing the transformation of a village boy from Tuban into a Javanese version of Marlon Brando in *The Wild One*, and I am being thoroughly entertained. Harto isn't, and neither is Galuh, nor her girls.

Sadly, this entertainment comes to an abrupt end. Not because Aji reverts back to his former self. Far from it! Not long after the motorbike has begun to change the status quo I develop a fever.

46

The first sign of dengue fever is a blinding headache that lasts for days. I was struck down twice in Bausasran and in both cases it took months to fully recover. The dengue fever virus is borne by the female *aedes aegypti* mosquito, which—if you examine under a magnifying glass—has deceptively pretty tiger stripes. If there is no sign of blood you are in luck, but if the one you catch has already fed you might be in trouble.

I could barely lift my head from the pillow on the morning I woke up with the tell-tale headache and high temperature of dengue fever—known in Indonesia as *demam berdarah.* Blood fever! My first thought was to take some paracetamol from the medicine bag I kept in the bedside drawer. The second was to ring the school. I was due to teach at midday and I had a sinking feeling I wouldn't be in.

Harold, the director, was immediately kind. I must have sounded as bad as I felt. He cracked a joke about the perils of living in a tropical climate and suggested I have a blood test as soon as I could. I switched off the phone and curled into the foetal position, adjusting the pillow under my head. By lunchtime the pain was unbearable.

Galuh arrived sometime after Dzuhur, the late morning call to prayer. Through the fog in my head, I heard her bicycle hit the rough concrete paving, then muffled talking in the kitchen, the rattle of pots and pans and the kettle whistle. Harto brought a bowl of beef-bone broth into the bedroom with sympathetic words.

"Don't be worried, Honey, you will get better soon," he reassured, sitting on the bed as he held a spoon to my lips. Honey, became his English term of endearment for me. I remember how surprised I was the first time I heard him say it. We were browsing in a Mata Hari department store. I'd stopped to take a closer look at a simple black shirt.

"That one will look good on you, Honey," he said shyly, as if experimenting with the English term. I hooked the hanger back on the rack taking his hand and allowing his words to clothe me instead.

Now I appeared to be very ill and beyond caring about clothing choices. Harto was spoon-feeding me beef-bone broth that Galuh had especially cooked. Spoon-feeding called *suapin* is an act of love in Java, for the ill and the healthy alike. Starry-eyed lovers or courting couples can often be seen in street-side warungs or restaurants spoon-feeding each other special dishes. Toddlers are often trailed by mothers and nannies holding spoons heaped high with rice.

Harto had little success spoon-feeding me that day, and the paracetamol was having no effect. I fished around the medicine bag and found some aspirin, took two tablets and crawled back into bed. I didn't think aspirin could do any harm. But dengue fever thins the blood and aspirin thins it further. The aspirin was taking its time to work. First the skin on my hands and feet began to burn from the inside out. Galuh bought fresh guava juice, a home remedy, insisting I drink, while Harto brought cool flannels for my feet and face.

For a few days I resisted going to hospital, even though there was a well-established one five minutes' walk away—and even though the decor appealed to my sense of romance in a rather nostalgic way. The virus had sapped the energy from every cell in my body, but when the signs of haemorrhagic fever surfaced in a spotty rash there were no further protests from me.

Harto, his face a mask of concern, bundled me into the car and drove around the corner to the hospital emergency department carrying me like a limp bride across the threshold. Then at the doctor's immediate instruction onto the blue sheet of a hospital trolley bed. The sight of linoleum floors and the sharp smell of disinfectant had never been so welcome, then the room began to spin and I blacked out.

Moments later I opened my eyes to a flurry of nurses in starched white uniforms with matching caps. One of them wheeled over an intravenous drip and attached the line to a vein. Blood tests were taken and medical details clipped onto the end of the bed with my name written in felt marking pen:

> Nama: Nonya Lara Davies
> Warga Negara: Australia

During the day, Harto, his face etched with worry, would shuttle back and forth to the hospital bringing foods he hoped might tempt. At night, he would sleep on the vinyl visitors bed in my room.

Saraswati came to visit in the mornings while Bhima was at school. She would offer sips of guava juice and special drinks she had made from *temulawak* root. We would pass the time talking about Bhima and his drum band practice, or that he was avoiding homework. About her mother Ibu Salim's ronde ginger tea stall at the late-night markets; about my students at the English school or her wedding kebaya customers. She would fuss about plumping the pillows and filling the water jug but mostly she would just sit with me in reassuring company. Her presence so considerately quiet you could have heard a pin drop. During this time, our friendship blossomed.

Towards the tail end of my hospital stay, I asked Harto to see if Galuh could steam some plain potatoes. My taste buds had turned metallic–as happens with dengue fever. I couldn't face another bowl of steely rice porridge. In my hazy-headed state, I must have said *wartol* instead of *kentang* because, like a magic trick gone wrong, Harto turned up with a container of boiled carrot! Still, it was the first time in days that we laughed, and we both fell about. But afterwards

I flinched at how much worse it made my head feel, because a dengue fever headache is like a crown of thorns—a form of torture.

Ten days after I was admitted to Bethesda hospital with its steel framed beds and nurses in starched uniforms, I was allowed to leave–released with a month's supply of cinnamon and turmeric capsules. And, in a large envelope the recent history of my platelet count.

Weeks later when I deciphered the numbers, I realised I had been rather close to death's door, but from the faces that surrounded me, I never suspected. Those beaming Javanese smiles had been the stronger medicine. Not everyone was confident I'd pull through, among them two visitors from the language school: Harold, the director of studies, and Carl, the hippie minister and head teacher.

Harold's usual jokes were self-effacing ones about his baldness. There were more bald jokes to come in the weeks that followed when they both deployed the best of British humour to keep my chin up because after the dengue fever abated, the hair that had been my pride (despite many arguments in the mirror) began to moult, and so for the first time in my adult life I got a pixie cut. But it didn't look as good as Leila's.

While I was away the students decorated my classroom with welcome back posters. They were excited to see me return. After the lethargy that lingered for weeks retreated, no one was more relieved than me. No one except Harto, whose facial muscles finally relaxed back in to his familiar smile.

While I was away, Galuh and Aji had managed the house together and done very well it seemed. The floors and furniture polished to a high sheen. The gardens clipped and green. I didn't suspect that Galuh had also been busy at the house gathering the seeds she needed to plant in my mind in order to usurp Aji's position.

--oOo--

There is no vaccination against dengue fever, which keeps a population alert, especially in regard to stagnant water. The smallest amount in a vase can become a breeding ground for mosquitos.

Before I got dengue fever, Harto would take me to the flower market to buy cut orchids and tuber roses. Aji never really had success growing them in the garden, though he tried his best. The colourful flower market, which ran down an entire street, had been a joy for me to discover. After the dengue fever episode, the only flowers allowed to decorate the house were either potted orchids or artificial.

When we set up the house in Bausasran, I bought two tall glass vases. Not long after, one went missing. After Aji left, I found it tucked away in the corner of a dark cupboard in the garden shed. There was a large chip on the base which had formed a crack. I didn't mind that it was broken, because for a moment it brought him back—his shyness and the birth of his confidence. He must have worried about the break. I imagine the vase slipped in the ceramic tiled sink when he was changing the water. I placed the second vase carefully beside it and closed the door on the dust that had accumulated since he left.

The days of perfumed flowers in vases of water had passed, as had the sight of Aji with his mop and his muscles and the sound of the broom as he swept the paths. By that time Galuh had taken the reins. She was doing her best to manage the chores, but she didn't have his muscled shoulders and she wasn't as naturally neat. Galuh's scheme to take over Aji's position had succeeded within a week of my coming home from hospital.

"Juragan, Aji is not working when you are at school. Aji is watching television all day. Aji is playing with girls all night. Why pay two people when I can do his job and mine? I can clean the garden just as well as Aji."

True, Aji had begun to bring girls home after midnight. I would hear the garage door creak open as he smuggled them in. One morning at breakfast, I caught sight of a sheepish girl in a short skirt sitting on a chair outside his bedroom. Aji apologised, saying it had been too late to take her back to her boarding house. She had stayed overnight in one of the spare rooms.

Galuh was glowering over the stove as she listened and I was beginning to see her point. But it was so hard to let him go because he had left an indelible mark, as if the henna he used to blacken his hair had brushed my heart. And, while I had watched him learn and grow, I had grown into myself.

Hoping some money would set him up for the future, I folded a small roll of rupiah notes inside a handwritten letter of thanks and good wishes. Harto said Aji would return to his village. At least he was away for the volcanic eruption of Mount Merapi—the giant smoking guardian to the north of Yogyakarta.

47

In late October 2010, Mount Merapi began to get moody; rumbling and smoking itself into a series of violent outbursts in the form of flying rocks and ash, and lethal gases. This mood lasted until early December by which time it had blown a significant amount off its top. On 25 October, when alert levels rose to their highest, Harold, the Director of Studies, sent everyone home from the language school.

For most of the next four weeks I was either glued to the laptop in the study, searching for information on pyroclastic flows, or sitting on the Persian rug, watching live broadcasts on Metro TV. Ninik and Rani came with their school books to study, casting worried glances whenever the windows rattled from either thunder or a mountain rumble. We could never be sure which, because the sounds mirrored each other or rolled in chorus. In those volatile weeks I learned a whole new set of vocabulary including:

gemuruh: the rumble of a volcano (or a rumbling stomach)
abu: ash
pasir: sand
kerikil: gravelly stones
wedhus gembel: plumes of smoke shaped like woolly sheep
lahar: lava.

According to my calculations Bausasran was far enough away for us not to be suffocated, or burnt alive like the poor people of Pompeii!

Tensions were building everywhere in Yogyakarta. Mbah Maridjan; the spiritual gatekeeper of Merapi, had been claimed by the scorching gases. The 83-year-old had chosen to override a warning given by Sultan Hamengkubuwono X, who had appointed him. He also chose to ignore the strong advice given by the leading volcanologist. His ash covered body was found with a group of villagers he had hoped to protect. By local accounts, their lives were ended while kneeling in prayer, pleading for mercy.

Fortunately, most of the villagers who lived on the slopes were already camping in evacuation centres by then, and as the dangerous radius surrounding the crater increased, tens of thousands of others joined them in order to prevent further catastrophe.

On a Saturday towards the end of October I woke up in the middle of the night to a crackling sound like dry leaves burning. Careful not to stir Harto I tiptoed outside to investigate. The sky was an eerie mix of charcoal grey and red. I held my hand out as if checking for raindrops but instead my palm was filled with grit. We were thirty kilometres away from the crater.

"That is *kerikil,* said Harto," appearing beside me. He put his arm around my waist and kissed my forehead. For a while we watched the firelit sky. By morning, the whole house, the gardens and paths and the big ceramic urns were blanketed in coarse sand and ash.

Harto dressed calmly and drove the Kijang over to check on Saraswati and her mother and Bhima. Soon, he brought them back, reporting that the whole city looked like the moon. He said the streets were choked motorbikes. The panic was causing collisions. Saraswati, looking shell-shocked, said every rider's face was covered with ash. After a brief debate we decided it was best if Harto took them straight to Wonosari village to shelter with extended family.

"The traffic is stuck everywhere, Lara, it might take some hours. Ask Galuh to stay with you?" he said, as he lifted Mbah Salim, his tiny mother-in-law, wrapped tightly in her batik sarong, onto the back seat of the Kijang, beside her sleepy grandson.

"Drive carefully, Harto, and take these extra masks Saraswati," I offered, through my own blue surgical one, before she climbed into the front seat and they drove off and down the street leaving tyre tracks in the ash.

A little later, Galuh arrived in a panic with a nervous Ninik and a wide-eyed Rani. She looked around for Harto, noting the absent Kijang. I told her where he had gone. She bit at her nails as she related news that a paranormal had predicted Merapi would erupt like Krakatoa.

"Yogyakarta will be erased from the map," she fretted. I tried not to let her fear infect me but it was a fast-acting contagion.

"Is it possible for Pak Hadi to drive you and the girls out of the city, Galuh," I asked, looking for a way to calm her.

Distraught and with tears streaming she pulled her blue Nokia cell phone from her back pocket and called him. Soon Pak Hadi arrived with his calming nature. He confirmed the streets were in chaos and, noting the ash covered kitchen benches and the drooping branches of the mango tree advised us to wear masks indoors as well as out.

"I will ask Harto to drive me to Jakarta when he returns," I told them, my rising fear overriding any rational calculations.

"Ya, ya, Juragan, you will be safer," agreed Galuh still sniffling.

"You and the girls should go now with Pak Hadi. Don't worry, I will explain to Harto," I reassured her, pushing them to go, knowing her relationship with her brother walked a tightrope at the best of times.

Harto returned late that night. His mood was broody. By that time, so was mine. Harto had forgotten to take his Nokia phone that morning. I had spent the day alone and confused about which belongings were essential for someone fleeing a volcano, and feeling that apart from two Nokia phones and a laptop, there were none.

"Sorry I couldn't contact you, Lara. I thought you would be okay with Galuh," he sighed, collapsing onto the Persian rug with driver fatigue, his bloodshot eyes staring blankly up at the chandelier.

"Pak Hadi has taken her somewhere safe. Ninik and Rani went too."

"Galuh is making everyone panic," Harto snapped. "We are safer here than on the roads."

I explained that I had pushed her to go. She had been in such a state over the paranormal's prediction. Smouldering on the Persian rug, he said not to worry about Galuh anymore. That she wouldn't be working at the house in Bausasran again. He would speak to her when she returned, whenever that might be.

After a day of driving in the heat and dust and smoke and tension, his sister was the straw that broke the camel's back. Afterwards he and Galuh never spoke to each other again.

Saraswati and Mbah Salim could help with the cooking, he decided, and Santi, his eldest sister, could help with cleaning. She would be happy to earn some extra money, he assured. And he himself would take over Aji's job.

"Please don't overload poor Saraswati with more cooking," I pleaded, insisting I could happily live on gurami fish and baby kialan from Cianjur seafood restaurant, and my favourite dish gudeg sagan. Despite this, she often sent him back from Surokarsan with beef rendang or a chicken curry, and sometimes special cakes called *apem* because she knew I sometimes missed bread.

I was surprised at how much I missed Galuh after she left. I missed the rattle of her bicycle and the way she pounded onions and spice, and I missed her smirks and smiles. I missed seeing her at the soft drink stand she set up in front of the house during the fasting month of Ramadan. Despite her faults she was industrious.

But I didn't miss her as much as I missed seeing Aji stroll past the windows of the study, carrying pruned branches from the garden—his shoulders so broad and straight. Or as much as I missed Ninik coming to practice English. Though I didn't miss Ninik as much as I missed little Rani. My heart still swells to think of her.

"When life throws you lemons, Rani, you must make lemonade," I once taught her from an old adage I'd heard somewhere. She recited it back to me not knowing that her smile would be all it took to fill a soda-fountain shop with bubbles.

A few weeks after the eruption we drove up to the village of Cangkringan, on the slopes of Mount Merapi. The ground was still hot and smoking, and the smell of dead livestock permeated the air. Harto remarked with sadness as we surveyed the scene, "This is like a ghost village."

He asked an old woman, "Where do you live, Ibu?" She nodded towards a dusty patch of land under a scorched coconut palm and answered with a vacant look, "My house was over there."

When all the chaos and destruction caused by Merapi's volcanic eruption had settled, a period of reconstruction began, just as it had after the earthquake five years earlier.

A few months after the eruption and Galuh's unfortunate departure, Harto demolished Saraswati's low-ceilinged house in Surokarsan and began building a better one with the black volcanic sand he dredged from the Code River.

Saraswati her mother and Bhima, moved in next door with Ayang Uti for the best part of a year. Her house was so cramped she would laughingly call it the chicken coup.

Harto worked the days at Surokarsan and spent the nights at Bausasran. It was exciting to see the bamboo scaffolding go up and the new house come together brick by brick; two levels, both with high-ceilings. As the house evolved, the gold jewellery on Saraswati's fingers gradually disappeared, until she had only one set of gold earrings and her gold wedding band left.

Eventually, she had a brand-new house with a bathroom on each floor. Mbah Salim had her own curtained-off room next to the kitchenette downstairs and Bhima had a small room upstairs next to the spacious master bedroom. It was wonderful to see Saraswati embracing the new space as she dusted and decorated.

48

The days in the house at Bausasran rolled on into months and years, until seven years had passed. They rolled on, as lessons at the English school morphed into lessons at Wisma Bahasa language school.

On Tuesdays I studied Indonesian literature with the bibliophile Maulina, becoming a fan of the popular author Dee Lestari and the famous poet Sapardi Djoko Damono. On Wednesdays I learned more about Yogyakarta from Pak Bayu, and on Fridays I took Javanese language lessons with Ibu Ningsih.

From Ningsih I learned that home could be either *omah*; *griyo* or *dalemipun*, depending on the level of conversation, and came to see how Javanese defines and refines a culture. But I only ever practiced with Harto for fear of offending someone.

Pak Bayu was an encyclopaedia of historical and geographical facts about Yogyakarta, and had a gift for drawing diagrams.

"Besides the famous Code River, Yogyakarta has the Gajah Wong and the Winoga, the Opak and the Oyo and Progo. In the Javanese language, we like the sound of O," he would joke. "Even if we write A, we say O."

Pak Bayu always addressed me with the polite term of mother. "Ibu Lara, the special region of Yogyakarta is the only place in Indonesia to still be governed by a sultan," he liked to explain, interspersing facts with local stories and legends.

Harto would drive me to these classes in the Kijang, as punctually as he had driven me to the teacher training course in Bali, and all the English lessons that followed. While I studied at Wisma

Bahasa he would go to work as usual, selling batik to tourists, in his familiar stomping ground of Jalan Malioboro.

With so many trips to school and back, and many trips to tourist places with visitors who came to stay, the old Kijang had thousands more kilometres added to the odometer and still it faithfully never missed a beat.

Pak Yuda would drop in with a bamboo basket, whenever he thought the mango trees had borne fruit, and once horrified Harto by helping himself to all the cream wafers in the big red and white tin of Khong Guan mixed biscuits we'd bought for Aji when he first arrived.

Five mornings a week, Harto's gentle-humoured oldest sister Santi, would work her magic on the tiled floors and bathrooms until they were gleaming. From time to time to my delight, Rani and Ninik would still drop in. There were regular sewing sessions with Saraswati that added new blouses to the collection we designed for teachers; blouses with comfortable sleeves for reaching the top of the whiteboards without baring the midriff. She taught me her deft way of making patterns with newspaper. In the cheval mirror she demonstrated how she pinned and fitted.

There were occasional visits from Amar and Alin, and for a few months, the fuss and excitement that came with the preparations for their Javanese wedding ceremony in Jakarta: the invitations to Amar's band of friends in Brisbane; the organisation of accommodation and the traditional costumes they would all wear, and Harto's search in Yogyakarta for the keris daggers the men would need to wear.

Alin had given me the task of having batik-patterned fans made in Yogyakarta as a momento for each guest. Meanwhile Harto sought out old money notes in the alley behind Pasar Beringharjo markets to be framed as a symbol of the *mas kawin* marriage gold. Amar and Alin had calculated an amount based on the auspicious date they met.

All of this was followed, two years later, by the birth of their daughter, Kee, and the swell in my chest at first sight of her in the nursery of the hospital in South Jakarta; then a month later her blessing with a traditional selamatan celebration.

More selamatan celebrations were held for the new-borns that Wanto and his wife added to their family in quick succession–filling the world with little replicas until we lost count of how many there were. Wanto and his wife had grown their own handbag and accessory business by then, earning enough to feed all their offspring. There were trips to the cemetery during Idul Fitri to sprinkle baskets of *bunga setaman* petals on Ibu Daliyah's grave. Bunga setaman is a garden mix of seven scented flowers: jasmine, magnolia, ylang-ylang and tuberoses, combined with red and white and pink or crimson roses, used for births, weddings, burials and other celebrations.

There were friendly house calls from Pak Sungkar and Yana, along with her cousin Dewi, whenever they drove to Yogyakarta to visit Tante Sarmini. They liked to tell us with an encouraging air, that Yana was planning to study psychology at Gajah Mada University when she finished high school. Dewi had gone to live at their cottage in Taman Pinang; taking my place on the return journey, and by all accounts sharing the care of the fluffy white cat with Yana as they travelled the same road back. Eventually Pak Sungkar remarried. "She is a widow," he told us, "a devout Muslim, a clever cook, and very kind to Yana."

There had been two banquet-style Christmas dinners at the long teak table in the kitchen with all the teachers from the English language school. Six small kampung chickens had been roasted–two at a time in the small oven with their heads and clawed feet still limply attached. Out of respect for his mother—and rightly so—Harto had refused to eat their headless, tasteless, hormone-fed cousins from the Superindo supermarket.

There were morning yoga stretches on the Persian carpet; cups of tea and deep friendships shared on its soft green and madder-red comfort.

From time to time, there were visits from friends or family members on international flights, stopping in as they passed through on their travels. Sheena would catch the Sanjaka train to stay with us whenever she had a holiday. The house in Bausasran welcomed them all with open arms.

Apart from the dengue fever episode, a rainy season house flood, Aji's departure, the volcanic eruption of Mount Merapi, a geological event that triggered so much tension it caused a smaller eruption of sibling tempers, there were only minor disruptions. Then Saraswati fell ill.

49

We were riding on the southern ring road towards the beach at Parangtritis, when Harto mentioned Saraswati had been to see the doctor. She had noticed flecks of blood in between her periods and suffered severe cramping. I remember that Saturday morning. The sky was a crystal blue, the sun shining brightly over the rice paddies as we rode with our visors up, the breeze brushing our faces. Harto had come from Surokarsan to pillion me on the old Honda. The moment he confided the news, it felt as if time stood still and the farmers in the fields stopped work, paused long enough for a cloak to descend and cover me. And then with a jolt the clock began to tick again but the mood had changed.

At the cliff-top lookout where we often sat, there was a small kiosk made from salvaged boards, run by a woman whose skin was just as worn. Harto ordered two young coconuts—our usual drinks. But that day, as she sliced off the tops with her trusty old machete, there wasn't the usual exchange of news, just the polite necessities. Bending her back she set the two coconuts on our usual low bamboo table overlooking the beach. She placed a flask of red plastic straws beside them. Though the sun glistened on the waves below our faces were sombre, our drinks barely touched.

"Try not to worry, Pang, she will be okay," I said, massaging away the nerves that were causing his thigh muscle to shudder. But inside I had a horrible feeling that the cloak belonged to the grim reaper. That it was the cloak of death. A premonition.

"The doctor has arranged for Saraswati to have a biopsy next week," he told me, staring into the layers of green and blue landscape.

"You will be okay, Pang. You might lose your footing sometimes, but I will never let you fall. You must be her strength now."

We didn't finish our coconut drinks that day, apologising profusely to our host. As we said goodbye to the old woman, a sudden gust of wind blew the container of red straws off the table and onto the ground, where they scattered.

--oOo--

The results of Saraswati's biopsy the following week returned a positive result for cervical cancer, early stage two. The cancerous cells had spread beyond the cervix and invaded her uterus. She would need a hysterectomy as soon as possible. When Harto came to Bausasran to tell me the following afternoon, his shoulders looked as slumped and heavy as the temple stones of Borobudur.

"There is a chance that Saraswati might not survive," he said, as he removed his helmet and slowly wheeled his Honda in under the pendopo. I took his heavy cardigan and hung it over a kitchen chair; brought him a glass of hot tea, the way he liked it—strong and without too much sugar.

"Here, Pang, please drink this to help you settle. I am so sorry to hear the news. My heart is breaking for you. How is Mbah Salim? Have you mentioned anything yet to Bhima? We will make sure Saraswati gets the best treatment possible. And you must stay with her now, both the days and the nights. She will need you close, Pang."

"She will need you too, Lara. She is very afraid. She wonders if you can accompany her in the hospital."

"Of course, Pang," I assured. "I will come to sit with her as she did for me when I was so ill with dengue fever."

When I said it, I had no inkling there would be more than just the days in the hospital. In the months of her illness that followed, I would bear witness to the most fitful of her nights.

"Pak Rohadi from next door can help with the gardens, Lara. I will speak with him now," he said, "and I will ask him to be the security guard too. He is honest. Tomorrow I will put another lamp in the front garden to warn off thieves."

"Don't forget your cigarettes on the table, Pang. And give Pak Rohadi the goat satay you brought for me. Thank you, but I'm not really hungry. I've already eaten *pecil* for lunch today with Maulina at Wisma Bahasa. We're reading a story by Dee Lestari. I have to translate some pages for homework. It's called *Heaven's Light*."

--oOo--

Pak Rohadi lived in a tiny security hut in the front garden of the big house next door. It was really nothing more than a tin shed with a kapok mattress on the ground and a charcoal stove with a wok for cooking. There was no electric light. Just a kerosene lamp hanging on a wire. The house he guarded had been a former boarding house for girls, but termite damage had caused the wood to weaken until the roof began to cave in.

"Pak Rohadi is from a village near Bantul to the south," Harto told me after they met. Since then, they had often passed time relaxing under the pendopo while I planned lessons in the study.

"Pak Rohadi is divorced," Harto told me. "His wife found someone who could give her more money." Later I learned from a neighbour's gossip that Pak Rohadi had one grown up daughter, university educated somehow, but she seldom visited.

We came to recognise the sound of Pak Rohadi's comings and goings by the clackety engine of his old red motor scooter. He wore thin, torn T-shirts and rubber flip-flops and he never wore a helmet.

Pak Rohadi, though painfully shy, had a big bold brush of a moustache that would have suited Wanto better. His pallor seemed a little yellow to me, and his stomach swollen. Enough to cause Pak Sungkar to comment–after meeting him on a visit, "these things can signal kidney trouble." And he would know.

Pak Rohadi's circumstances had always worried me, so I was more than happy to offer him a job. He never once missed a day. In the mornings I would wake to hear him at work with his polishing cloth on the windowpanes. "How is Pak Harto's wife?" were about the only words he ever spoke. For the long months that Saraswati was ill, I felt as though Pak Rohadi was a gift from God.

50

Saraswati's cancer took over her body like a wartime invasion of troops, fitted with angry new boots and weapons. Bloodthirsty. Relentless. Ravaging her body. Leaving a few limp cells to burn on slow torture. And then, after almost a year of this, blowing them out with a satisfied puff. Only then did the enemy pack up and leave.

Neither Harto, the only soldier on her side, nor the house he had built with so much love could protect her. That was a heart-wrenching scene to watch as again and again he reassured her she would get better, knowing the surgeon who had performed her hysterectomy, and a few months later operated again to make a stoma, gave no hope at all. The six weeks of chemotherapy had failed and the radiation treatments had obstructed her bowel. We brought her home from hospital in a wheel chair for palliative care. By then she was skin and bone.

"We will keep this knowledge from Saraswati, it is the Javanese and most humane way," said Harto. All of Saraswati's relatives and all the neighbours agreed it would be cruel for her to know her fate. They decided it was best not to tell Bhima or Mbah Salim either. I wrestled with thoughts about whether they were right or not, but I was there to support not to interfere.

The initial wait for a hospital bed at Sardjito public hospital had lasted almost two months. Every day Harto had called to check for available beds but was told the rooms were full.

Saraswati fretted through those weeks, pacing from the kitchen to the front door and back in her daster dresses and always behind her like a shadow was the tiny form of her mother Mbah Salim, her face paralysed with fear as she tried to spoon-feed her only daughter fried offal meats for strength. For the first time in forty years Mbah Salim stopped selling ginger tea in the palace square at night.

But her daughter had no appetite. The chemotherapy had made her constantly nauseous. Her weight was dropping daily until she was too weak to climb the stairs to her bedroom. At least her thick, waist length hair had not fallen out. Harto made up a bed for her on the living room floor. It was easier for the palliative nurses to give the transfusions she needed to replace her increasingly blood-coloured urine.

From the middle of March until late May 2015 when Saraswati passed away there was a constant stream of relatives and neighbours dropping in. They would bring fruit or special foods and smile when they greeted her, then hide tears as they turned to leave. Some would sit with her on the mattress, others on chairs at the table from the house in Taman Pinang, by then covered with Ziplock bags and bottles of pills.

There were so many pills and capsules and they were hard for her to swallow. Harto would coax them into her with spoonfuls of agar-agar jelly. At least the palliative nurses in their blue cotton jilbabs, long skirts and aprons could administer the strongest painkillers through an intravenous drip.

Saraswati's cousin Siti was the most adept at changing the stoma bag; much more confident than Harto and me. She worked at Sardjito hospital as a cleaner, but she was sharp enough to be an eye surgeon, taking notice of everything the nurses did as she mopped around them. Her ten-year-old daughter Raisa was just as alert, as she watched her mother's skilled hands. Siti confided that years before Saraswati fell ill; she'd had a premonition. "I had a *firasat,*" she confided. Since then, she suspected her cousin would not have a long life. Between us we agreed to tell Saraswati and her mother the stoma bag was temporary, just until she got better. It calmed their fears. That is kinder, Siti said.

In early April Saraswati's right leg began to swell and the blood in her urine increased until the blood transfusions were having no effect. The palliative nurses sensed it was time for Bhima to say goodbye to his mother. To relieve Harto, I took Bhima down to a quiet spot on the river.

"Bhima, you better sit with your mother for a while," I advised him gently. "You must tell her all the things you want her to know." He sobbed, "So, I will never go shopping with Ibu again?"

After comforting him for a while we trudged back up the hill to the house. Seeing him so awkwardly exposed as he knelt to whisper his final words to his mother, I hastily shuffled all the women in their daster dresses out through the front door. This act of mine became a lasting bond between Bhima and me.

That night Harto and I slept on the floor, on either side of Saraswati. In the morning I heard the broadcast of a resident who had died the day before, and knew that soon it would be Saraswati's name they announced. For the next three days she was in a state of delirium.

51

Neither Harto nor I were there when Saraswati took her final breath. She died just before dusk. Harto had gone to pay for her palliative care and was held up by a long queue. I had gone back to the house in Bausasran to rest, forgetfully leaving a soft woollen scarf behind on Saraswati's bed. I had just showered when Harto called to say he had arrived back at Surokarsan minutes after Saraswati passed away.

"I'm so sorry, Pang, I will be there soon," I comforted, my chest swelling in sadness as I hung up and dialled for a taxi to take me back to Surokarsan. When I arrived, the house was filled with family members and neighbours. Ayang Uti was weeping inconsolably. I weaved through the tight crowd to where Saraswati's lifeless body lay covered in a sarong on her bed. The soft scarf I had left behind was wrapped around her face–binding her jaw, as if the god of small things had arranged it earlier. I searched for Harto and found him slumped on the front step with a steady arm around Bhima whose face was pale and blotched from tears. For a while I sat with them. Then suddenly the world around us began to move quickly.

A few curious men nearby disappeared back to their homes. Harto and Bhima excused themselves and climbed upstairs to sit on the balcony and wait for Maghrib prayers. Only the women were allowed to stay, including wide-eyed little daughters and teenage girls who watched this lesson on death unfold, as I did.

The kampung funeral specialist appeared carrying a white burial cloth. She was strikingly tall with an unusual mop of floppy silver curls. She began to call instructions, competently directing the residents as if she had done it countless times before. In an instant a steel divan was set up beside the well. Then plastic buckets were filled from the outside tap and sprinkled with crimson and cream petals. Saraswati's body would be bathed seven times in this flower-scented water.

"Mbak Lara, please join us for the ritual bathing of Saraswati," insisted Ayang Uti, her face all puffy with tears as she took my hand and pulled me down the front steps.

"Come, come, Mbak Lara," cried Ibu Imaro.

"Come, Mbak Lara," cried Lastri.

"Come with us," cried Siti.

What a gift to be chosen as one of the seven women to ladle the rose petal water over Saraswati's body. My gratitude was beyond words. Each ladle–poured from her head to her feet was said with a prayer. Mine was the last, and with it the women's faces lifting my spirit in the solidarity of this final loving act. All the while Mbah Salim sat and watched silently from behind the open front door, a tiny defeated figure. She was a mother who had just lost her one beloved child, surely the hardest pain of all.

After the bathing ritual, Saraswati's body was lifted from the steel divan by the women, and laid out on tikar mats in the front room. Her body was then perfumed and embalmed. As I sat with the women and watched the proceedings, Ayang Uti's daughter-in-law broke down in tears, struggling to arrange the wet straggling strands of Saraswati's hair as she folded pieces of soft cotton cloth to cover her eyes.

That night, Mbah Salim climbed the stairs she had never climbed before and slept beside me in Saraswati's bed. During the night I woke to her moaning in distress and rubbed her back until she fell back to sleep. Harto kept vigil for most of the night with Bhima, then they slept a few hours on a woven tikar mat downstairs.

The next morning, I awoke to the sound of water being ladled downstairs, and the warbling of Harto's pigeons on the roof calling for yesterday's rice. *Wok-wok-kethekurrr, wok-wok-kethekurrr*.

Mbah Salim as usual was up at dawn to cook rice as she always did, grounding herself with the daily chores. I could hear Ayang Itu's voice above the chatter of the kampung women in the alley below. They had begun cooking curries for the selamatan to be held in the evening. The smell of garlic and chilli was wafting up into the bedroom. Harto brought two glasses of tea and boiled eggs for breakfast. Soon the kampung loudspeaker broke through these morning signs of life with the sad announcement we were expecting:

> "Saraswati, forty-three years old, daughter of Bapak and Ibu Salim, husband of Bapak Harto, mother of Bhima, passed away last evening. The funeral will begin at one o'clock."

Wanto arrived early, wearing a gold trimmed prayer shirt and peci. He comforted Mbah Salim, then exchanged a few words with Bhima and Harto. After the prayer ceremony led by the Imam, he joined the men who would push Saraswati's divan with its orange umbrellas to the cemetery. I went by foot with the women who followed, all of us wearing scarves or jilbab. Despite the midday heat we ran to keep up. As we puffed and sweated, the women told me the spirit of the deceased sets the speed. The divan was hurtling along the street ahead of us with its bright umbrellas leading the way. Saraswati must have wished for a fast burial. From somewhere, someone threw handfuls of coins to mark the way. They clinked as they fell on the asphalt and scattered. The women said the coins were a prayer for Saraswati's safe journey.

At the cemetery, I watched with Harto, Bhima and Wanto as three men climbed into a deep grave. Then I watched three more lower Saraswati's body, wrapped in white, into the arms of the ready men. They placed her body in the foetal position on her right side and unwound the top twist of the pocong cloth so her face touched the soil. Then to my surprise they placed wooden planks half way up. Strangely, I felt relief, as if the space would let her breathe. Then Harto said, "Look over there, Lara. Do you see the mute man signing to Bhima?" "Oh yes, Pang, he is camouflaged against the trees."

The night before Saraswati passed away a ragged mute man was seen walking past the front door of Saraswati's house. He appeared again and hovered a moment during her flower petal bath. Later that evening he appeared for the third time in the community meeting room where the overnight prayer vigil for Saraswati was held. He signed to Harto about the scheduled time for the funeral the following day. Harto signed back—1 o'clock. The mute man appeared again at the cemetery directing Bhima on how to scatter the flowers over his mother's grave from head to feet. Harto said the young man was known in Yogyakarta as an angel of death. He said there were two brothers–both mute; wherever they went, people offered food and transport. Harto believed they had a sixth sense for knowing when good people are about to die. I thought, with his pointy chin and wispy beard he could have been the faun god Pan.

Ibu Salam had been unable to watch her daughter's interment. She sat on a headstone a few metres away. She wore, as usual, a batik sarong and one of the kebaya that Saraswati had made for her in happier times. Oddly, she had worn a black jilbab rather than a kerudung scarf to match her traditional clothes, as though lost without Saraswati's eye and attention to detail. It would be months before her tears flowed.

After all the prayers were spoken and the flower petals sprinkled, we turned to leave and I noticed a single red rose on a scraggly tree near Saraswati's grave.

"Look Pang, a rose in full bloom. Nature's gift to Saraswati."

Leaving, we stepped carefully in single file between all the graves to the porch entrance and washed our feet following the Islamic custom. Ibu Salim, her face drawn with sadness, pushed some rupiah notes into the donation box for the grave keeper. Ibu Jumilah, her older frailer sister came to her side, followed by her strong nieces Siti and Lestari. They helped her home. Bhima returned with a group of school and kampung friends.

Together, Harto and Wanto and I walked slowly back along the road to Saraswati's house of sand and steel. Our hearts were heavy but the camaraderie was enough to help Harto pull his slumped shoulders up just a little. It would be a while before he could carry himself like a born soldier again.

When we got back to the kampung I ran into Bhima on the stairs. His long lashes were wet with tears as he implored "Mom Lara, promise you will not leave."

"Don't worry, Bhima, I will stay as often as I can."

After the funeral came the *selamatan* gatherings. Selamatan means safe journey in Indonesian. These good wishes are reinforced with prayers and the sharing of specially prepared food.

For a few nights after Saraswati passed away, Mbah Salim set out a tray of food in the belief that her spirit may be confused and come to the house. The neighbours tell me children can see them.

There is a series of traditional selamatan after a funeral. These roughly coincide with the stages of decomposition of the human body: seven days, forty days, one hundred days, then on each anniversary for three years, until one thousand days have passed. Then a headstone is erected to mark the grave, as happened after Ibu Daliyah passed away.

I would spend much of my time in Surokarsan over the next two years and join in the preparation of food for all of these selamatan gatherings, developing a close friendship with Mbah Salim and the women of the kampung. Mbah Salim went back to selling *ronde* ginger tea and roast corn at her night stall. Often Harto and I would accompany her until the early hours of the morning. Meanwhile, the house in Bausasran remained as always, our private haven.

Part Four

52

After an almost decade-long separation from Angus he calls from Jakarta to say he is ready to settle down with a young woman.

"She has a child," he tells me. "The father refused to take responsibility. I've moved her into the house. I feel so much for her."

I was hearing the same record that he had played in Solo all those years ago, after the lessons with Ibu Tjoe. "I feel so much for her". But I didn't want to hear it anymore because there had been other Ibu Tjoe's over the years, and I no longer cared.

"Best if we get a divorce then," I said.

"Why are you being so dramatic Lara? I've looked after you financially, haven't I? I've been generous and consistent. That won't change. I'm not planning to marry." But I'd heard that before too.

"In financial matters yes, that's true Angus and thank you. I have been more than grateful for the lifebuoy. And of course, Harto will be forever thankful to you for meeting the costs of Saraswati's medical care. But in matters of my heart, you failed me. You pushed me overboard and left me drowning."

Harto and I were driving when Angus called that day, so he pulled over into a dirt car park across the road from the Plaza Hotel. Somehow, he must have known the call was important. Though I had the phone pressed to my ear, he could hear the conversation and the mood. Hear Angus raise his voice in anger and frustration. But of course, the words I exchanged that day were not as composed as the ones that hindsight has more concisely shaped. In fact, I was frightened and I tripped and stumbled over all the answers I gave, just as I always had with Angus.

I had met and become his devotee when I was only nineteen years old–in awe of him and still too young to be discerning. Over the years he had become more and more a dominating father figure. We never complemented each other like other couples I saw, like Amar and Alin, like sun to garden flowers.

Perhaps Angus and I should have had checked the dates on the Javanese calendar, or spoken to a paranormal who may have foreseen the future because the cosmic matchmaker that I relied upon—the one who orchestrated the blooming of the cactus flowers on the wedding night—must have mistaken the stars and planet alignment for a different couple. Or read them with Amar in mind.

"Lara…Lara! You don't have to accept his anger. Just divorce him," says Harto, snapping me out of my reverie and back to the dirt car park with the open bins beside it smelling of rats and rotten peels.

"Huh! Oh, sorry Pang. I was trying to organise a few thoughts."

"You will get dizzy thinking too much, Lara."

"You're right about that, Pang."

"I just want to say I support you. You must fight back. Don't let him control you. If you need to look for advice in Australia, just do it."

"Yes Pang, I will need to go back for a short time. Who knows, I may even need to call on the powers of Roro Jonggrang!"

"From the angry voice I heard on your phone, Lara, you may need Dewa Shiva."

"Yes Pang, Lord Shiva, is a good choice but not to destroy Angus. Just the marriage bond."

"Do you still have the little bronze statue of Buddha, I gave you," he asks.

"Yes Pang, it's one of my treasures. How you ever found it on the ground that day is a miracle. It's no bigger than a button."

"My eyes are sharp, like a knife, Lara."

"Your eyes are like crystal diamonds Pang. Protecting me."

"But my eyes cannot be with you in Australia, Lara. Remember to take the Buddha."

"Yes Pang, see here it is in the palm of my hand. I always carry it with me."

"Aah, good, says Harto, turning the ignition key and finally breathing out the last of his fumes. "Just put your phone on silent. Don't answer if he calls again."

When Harto heard the way Angus raised his voice that day, his own anger began to stir and shot the whites of his diamond-cut eyes blood red. A suppressed anger rivalling the cauldron of molten rock that simmers inside Mount Merapi. As I sat in the passenger seat listening to his slow measured words I thought, "God help the island of Java, and Angus if there is another eruption of that temper. God had not helped Galuh to escape its fury."

"I will take you to Garuda Airlines in Jalan Malioboro to look for some flights now, Lara. Hopefully you will come back soon."

"Thank you, Pang, I hope so too," I say, resting my eyes on his familiar profile as we join the traffic on Jalan Gejayan already feeling how much I will miss him beside me.

53

I flew out of Sukarno Hatta Airport a week later filled with sadness, uncertainty and trepidation. All I had was a semi-hatched plan to secure half a house in my name in the hope it would give me some control of the shaky financial future I had still tied to Angus. I hoped to return within weeks with good news for Harto. I was wrong about everything.

When I arrived back in Australia in April 2017, I felt like a fish floundering on the beach, screaming for somebody to put me back into the water. Filled with dread I wanted to swim as fast as possible in the other direction, but nobody threw me in. Nobody knew I was drowning in the land-down-under air. But there were many kind people with fishponds who saw me and felt I needed to be kept alive.

These people were my friends and my family. But it was mostly the women who held me firm. My mother-in-law who loved me as much as I loved her; my born sisters, and; my sisters-in-law who had carried me through all the pain of Angus leaving and beyond, and one particular friend—my equivalent of Harto's friend, Wanto.

My friend Maria picked me up at Brisbane International Airport twelve years after she had dropped me off. The conversation carried on as though not a day had passed. She picked me up in the same black BMW that she always drove. The one she loved. The one she always said was better company than a bad husband. Maria was funny. If she hadn't achieved such high marks in typing and shorthand at school, she could have been a stand-up comedian.

She had a pageboy haircut like Galuh with the same kind of sassy fringe and she had a pretty face—milk white skin and brown eyes and she didn't age. This was because she kept a little weight on.

"That's the secret, Lara. Don't let yourself get too thin."

"Aah, Maria, it's so good to see you again. You sound like Harto. He's always telling me to eat more."

"I'm disappointed he didn't come with you, Lara."

"I know Maria. He is very fond of speaking with you on the phone. But he couldn't leave Saraswati's mother or Bhima. They still need him. I couldn't be that selfish. And I'm hoping this lawyer business won't take long."

"By the look of that small travel bag, let's hope not, Lara. Is that all you brought?"

"Yes Maria, just the bare necessities as you always taught me." And with that we break into an old chorus,

"Passport! Ticket! Wallet! Anything else you can buy!"

Because this was not the only time that Maria had either dropped me at the airport or picked me up. Maria had been there all the times I went back and forth to visit Harto in the beginning.

"It was heart-breaking to hear about Saraswati, Lara."

"Yes Maria, we are so lucky to have free pap smears here."

"I'll say, Lara. I'll never complain about the embarrassment again."

We drove at a confident speed from the airport down the double lane expressway into the city. Besides the familiar smell of Maria's Miss Dior parfum, I could smell tan bark and eucalyptus trees and I feared that smell would trap me in Brisbane. Trap me like a North Queensland cattle farmer slamming the last star picket into a barbed wire fence. And that feeling proved to be right. I would be breathing the smells of Australia for longer than I planned.

54

Maria had been the personal assistant to the CEO of a big firm in the city for many years, and she had connections.

"You need to ask a solicitor where you stand with the house, Lara. I'll give you the name of a woman you can trust."

By this time, we were sitting in a café. It was the same café where years before I had first shown her a photo of Harto, and she'd said he was handsome, and looked like a nice man. Neither of us knew he was married to Saraswati then. We just continued to drink our lattes and smile at my good fortune. We weren't smiling as much this time. The mood was much more serious, because Maria had a sixth sense for when trouble was brewing. As she sat back and listened to more and more of the details that I would need to mention to the solicitor our coffees went stone cold.

"Let me loan you a car for a few weeks Lara. Come over to my house whenever you like. I'll make my minestrone soup."

"Oh, I've missed your Italian cooking, Maria. Your minestrone is like a bowl of medicine."

"My two boys were raised on it, Lara. And you've seen the muscles on them."

"Yes, Maria, just like Amar. Our babies are all grown up. Oh Maria, I'm lucky to have you, thanks for all your kindness."

"Lara, remember you were there for me when I needed you."

I drove through Brisbane on all the same roads that I had before, but my heart was pumping in fear. Fear of driving and fear of the future.

Maria had loaned me a car that she had bought for one of her sons but he was taking a while to get his license. I didn't drive as confidently as Maria that day; I drove more like the son who was just learning. I ended up driving that car for a year after that day and shared many bowls of minestrone soup with Maria, and many tears.

As I drove, I remembered how brave Harto had been when I asked him to get his car-driving license and his nerves on the first night he drove me home from the language school in the Kijang. How I couldn't stop smiling at the views you don't get from a motorbike. I pictured the near collisions with pedicabs as he maneuvered the wide girth of it through the narrow streets of Yogyakarta, and how later he became a king of the road. He learned to drive a car because he couldn't see me disappointed, and because he knew how the motorbike helmet played havoc with my hair.

The next day, I pulled out the page of notes Maria had written for me, so I wouldn't forget all the important points. Her secretarial skills never switched off. Nervously I called the solicitor's number and made an appointment for the following week. In the meantime, I spent a lot of time debriefing with Maria.

"I'll have to get used to driving again, Maria. I'm so used to Harto driving me everywhere," I explained, as we sat on her back verandah one afternoon, looking out over a verdant lawn, lined with terracotta pots full of pastel pink geraniums.

"You'll be okay, Lara. But you're getting thinner by the day. Harto won't be happy. Maybe you should see Marlene, your doctor. She might prescribe some pills to help you get through this."

"Oh, I meant to say I saw her yesterday, Maria. She said it's no surprise I'm feeling anxious. She suggested I see a psychologist. I've chosen a man from the list she wrote down. I need strategies on dealing with a dominant male from one of the same species."

"Good plan, Lara, let me know how you go."

"Hi Maria, you'll never guess! I blurted out when I called her later. "The psychologist turned out to be the former sports coach from Amar's old school. He said he wondered if there was a connection when he saw my file and read the background letter I wrote. We bonded straight away. He smiled a lot when we talked about Amar. He mentioned how athletic he was at school and how good-natured. I told him Amar still played hockey; even when he lived in Jakarta, and now that he was back in Australia, he was skating again and sometimes sailboarding too, and that he had married a girl from Solo in Java, and they had a daughter. He just kept smiling and nodding more and more. And then he said Amar would always be fine, because he had a close-knit set of friends and, well, because I was crying so much about everything.

"Oh Lara, did he give you any tips?"

"He said an X-ray of my brain would probably look like Sydney in peak-hour traffic. He suggested as much walking as possible and gardening if I could. And he said to eat a lot of green vegetables, because science has proven that greens help with mental health."

"My mother could have told you that, Lara. And don't forget to smother everything in olive oil," she joked, in a response designed to cheer me up.

"Maybe I'll spend some time with Grace and Stephanie on their property up in the country. They have an organic vegetable garden and they're always inviting me to spend time there." Stephanie, being Angus's youngest sister and Grace being her partner.

"The only problem is a poor Internet connection, being so far from the city. Harto and I won't be able to video call each other as we have been daily."

"Just do it Lara. You need the fresh air. He'll understand, and he'll wait for you. Harto always waits for you."

"Yes Maria, that's true. Anyway, I spoke with Angus' sister Amy afterwards. She invited me for a beach walk at Shorncliffe on the weekend. Come if you like."

"You know me, Lara. I prefer to zip around in my car, but say hello to Amy, and look for the gelato shop across from the park. That's good therapy. Try the lemon."

Before any walks got underway, I was back at Maria's house in a state of distress.

"So, tell me about the phone call to Angus," she asked.

"He won't agree to an even split, Maria."

"There are laws, Lara. He can't just lord it over you. I'm sure your father would be telling you that if he was still here."

"If only he was, Maria. He was such a good lawyer and a good man. The only time he ever raised his voice was to sing at the piano when he played 'A Wonderful World' and turned into Louis Armstrong's trumpet."

"Well, you need to turn into Helen Reddy now, Lara, 'I am woman, hear me roar!' Have you made an appointment with the solicitor yet?"

"I'm seeing her next week. I need to get my thoughts in order."

"Lara, it's time to summon your inner lioness!"

"I might need the powers of a lioness and a boxer wrapped into one, Maria. Anyway, thanks for your company and the extra serving of minestrone for Kathleen."

"Don't forget a splash of good quality olive oil on top, Lara."

"Thanks Maria, I'll get a bottle of cold-pressed on the way home, though I hate supermarket shopping without Harto beside me."

When I arrived back at my mother-in-law's rescue pond, where I had been staying since I got back, it was getting dark. I put the kettle on.

"How about some tea, Kathleen," I asked her, as I took two cups from the tall pantry, knowing the answer to this question would be a cheery yes. She had never said no to sharing a pot of tea together, and often all my worries too.

"A worry shared is a worry halved," she liked to say. Kathleen was raised in a big Irish family that shared what little they had. I know she loves all her siblings. And I know she loves her seven children, as much as I love Amar. And that she loves them equally, including Angus.

Sitting on the sofa, I watched her familiar face from across the room, where she sat in her favourite chair with her white hair; and her reading glasses, and of late a tremor that said the puppeteer would not repair the strings that worked her hands, and my heart went out.

"Kathleen, I've brought you some minestrone soup from Maria. I've already eaten with her. Let me fix you a bowl."

"That was very thoughtful of her, Lara, and I've made a chocolate pudding for dessert."

"The smell invited me through the front door, Kathleen. I'm sure your chocolate pudding recipe will go down in history."

"Well, if you pass it on to Alin, I should confess it isn't mine. I got it from the Original Women's Weekly Cookbook, and most of the recipes I've cooked over the years. I've just added my own touch."

"Touch is the most important ingredient, Kathleen, and speaking of good cooks Grace and Stephanie have invited me to stay for a while."

"The country air is just what you need, Lara. It will do you the world of good. Enjoy it. And remember there's always a bed for you here."

55

I would spend the next few months at Grace and Stephanie's property in the country interspersed with trips to Kathleen's 'pond' and a family lawyer in Brisbane. My idea of a short trip back to Australia faded as rapidly as my anxiety levels rose. There were more minestrone soup meetings with Maria and strolls along seafront esplanades with Amy, involving my fears and tears, her consoling words, and lots of lemon gelato.

As the weeks went by, I stopped crying as much as I had when I first arrived. The therapeutic qualities of friendship along with Grace and Stephanie's organic garden were taking effect, but not as much as the line of homegrown philosophy that popped out of Stephanie's mouth one afternoon when we were picking snow peas in the vegetable patch.

"I'm so grateful to you and Grace for having me, Stephanie, but I'm struggling to find a purpose. I'm really not okay."

"You don't need a purpose, Lara; the only purpose of life is to live it!"

This surprise revelation had slipped out from under Stephanie's sunhat unexpectedly, just as her basket of peas reached full capacity, surprising us both into giggles. Sometimes it just takes a simple expression to strike a chord, or the right person to say it. Those words resonated with me. I still had panic attacks to overcome. The neural pathways of my brain still needed space and time to repair.

One day, Stephanie and Grace said they thought I was looking much better, and there was no need to keep playing the Joe Cocker CD. They laughed saying they understood how much I appreciated them without repeatedly singing, 'I get by with a little help from my friends.' Especially since we all sang the chorus off key. They were so accommodating to anything that might help to lift me up. But enough was enough. So, I said, "Sure, just play whatever music you like but not 'Send in the clowns', because it was the most depressing song ever written; and would upset me more because Amar was so frightened when he first saw a clown that he cried inconsolably. Just talking about it made tears well up in my eyes. Made me miss the baby version of him. And that made Stephanie even tearier, which worried Grace. In fact, all this weepiness was really distracting Grace, as she sat attempting to write poetry reviews of the all the paperbacks piled beside her on the sofa.

She suggested perhaps less talking and some different music—though she didn't really say 'less talking'. What she said very politely was,

"How about Fleetwood Mac. We haven't played their album for a while. It might lift our moods."

But it just made me more nervous because I knew she had to concentrate, and that the slightest movement, especially her getting up off the sofa might cause a landslide of books as big as the one Stevie Nicks had penned the lyrics about. All this was because, over the previous weeks, I'd developed a panic disorder and everything felt out of proportion. The best I could do, was remember to breathe.

"Thanks Grace," I mumbled. "That would be really nice."

Stephanie commented that we'd probably had too many cups of tea for one Saturday, and that the tannins might be counteracting the nutritional benefits of the organic salads. Then she decided that since the sun had set, we could have gin and lemonade instead. For therapeutic purposes; and because the lemon tree was producing so much fruit, we needed to either freeze the juice, make lemon cordial or use them to garnish our glasses.

All the excess fruit reminded me of Pak Yuda, but I stayed quiet because I was worried about how Grace was ever going to finish the poetry reviews. And I was worried because Grace and Stephanie were a couple and by now must be missing their together space, which was exactly what I was missing with Harto. I was missing the space that we created when we were alone together. But Grace and Stephanie always had stamina for friends and sisters and mothers in trouble. Grace, like my father was Welsh, and had the same strong 'yeoman' shoulders. Stephanie was a Scorpio who, like my mother, sometimes needed to take to the stage and sing soprano.

The more gin and lemonade she sipped, the more apologetic she became about how the unstable Internet connection was affecting my contact with Harto. And that reminded her of having met him when she and Grace came to stay at the house in Bausasran five years earlier. And how he'd taken her to Parangtritis while Grace was taking a batik painting class in the studios behind Jalan Sosrowijayan.

Then Grace remembered how, when Stephanie and Harto came to collect her, Stephanie's face looked pale. Someone had actually drowned at Parangtritis beach and the body dragged onto the sand.

She and Harto had witnessed the whole sad event. That's when Harto told her the story of Nyi Roro Kidul, the jealous goddess of the South Seas—the same story that he had told me years before. Stephanie said she was impressed by Harto's fluency in English. My pride swelled into a broad smile remembering his first efforts.

All this nostalgia reminded Stephanie of the batik fabrics she had bought in Yogyakarta. This recollection, combined with the jolly effects of the gin, seemed to spark her next incentive, otherwise she had already devised a project to distract me.

Wasn't this the perfect opportunity for Stephanie to add some new dresses to her wardrobe? Because after all, here I was, miraculously sitting at the dinner table in front of her with my professional design and pattern making skills just wasting away!

The fresh country air, the conversation and Stephanie's natural effervescence began to prompt a flood of fashion ideas. I wasn't sure Grace would ever manage to write the poetry reviews with all these ideas hatching around her.

"Grace!" she sang out, completely forgetting not to interrupt someone so deeply immersed in thinking.

"We'll be eating at the low coffee table for a few weeks. I'm turning the dinner table into a workbench for Lara. Can you help me to put the machine up?"

"What machine are you talking about, Stephanie?"

"Lara's mother's old Singer. It's somewhere in the shipping container!"

Between Fleetwood Mac songs and Stephanie's new plan, Grace finally abandoned the books on the sofa and decided to bake a loaf of bread instead. She said the kneading 'might' help her focus on the poetry reviews, and she could write them tomorrow. She was using all the polite modals. Could, and would, and might. As I sat and watched her from the kitchen table, my drink turning warm, I hoped the kneading would help her too. I still hadn't relaxed as much as they both hoped I would, so I got up and tipped the dregs of my glass into the sink in favour of herbal tea.

As soon as Grace saw me put the kettle on her smile beamed across the bench from the floury breadboard,

"Could I have a cup of that lemon myrtle tea too, Lara?"

And that smile helped me remember that it was okay to take the initiative with simple things like making tea or cooking dinner, because there was no Galuh or Aji or Santi here to help. Women in Australia do everything themselves. I knew I'd been sitting on a paling fence between two cultures since I got back because I was so afraid of falling into a mangrove swamp and never finding my way back to Harto.

There was more readjusting to be done besides just serving tea. There was conversation at mealtimes to get used to again; dry bathrooms and no spoon-feeding; no rice cookers sitting on benches as a matter of course; grocery shopping alone; and being in the driver's seat again without a palace carriage driver. The house in Bausasran, whose walls had wrapped around me so securely for all those years, was becoming more dreamlike in my memory. I'd been fighting a battle on the inside. Resisting. Not wanting to open my eyes. Scared if I immersed myself fully in the country where I was raised, I would never get back to Java, the place I had grown to love much more.

I fished Grace's favourite cup out of the cupboard. The fine porcelain one with the daffodils painted on it; and I made her that cup of lemon myrtle tea. I refused to let either of them go rummaging through the shipping container, now it was dark. Then we all agreed to leave it until the next day—Sunday.

Except for cleaning out the chicken coup and laying new straw, Sundays were for relaxing. Though, for Stephanie, that relaxation time was taken up with reading an unpublished manuscript written by an Australian author during the 1950s. A woman who had not received the same recognition her male counterparts had enjoyed. Stephanie was deciphering some handwritten letters sent between two people over the weeks of my stay. She began to suspect that that the parties involved might have been more than just friends.

"More likely friends," I nodded. "Like Harto and me."

While Grace and Stephanie were staying at the house in Bausasran, they bought some batik paintings. These now hung with a collection of artworks on the living room wall, creating an environment conducive to even more design. Well, that's what we thought as we drank our lemon myrtle tea and gazed around the cathedral ceilinged walls.

"Tomorrow morning, I'll look for the batik fabrics I bought in Jalan Solo, Lara."

"Do you have any ideas for designs, Steph?"

"Yes, something like the kebaya blouses that Saraswati taught you to make. There's a reconciliation conference coming up in Canberra. According to the forecast the weather will be hot, but I don't want to show my upper arms in public now I've turned fifty!"

"Steph, you're starting to sound as Javanese as I feel."

"Apart from her cute freckled nose," quips Grace.

"How about making something with the Indigenous prints you brought back from Ikuntji Art Centre last year?" I suggest, as the memory of a road trip she took filters into my thoughts. "Wouldn't it be a wonderful way to respect the country's original custodians?"

"Yes! It would be a way of showing solidarity and respect, and the batik from Yogyakarta will promote Indonesia, another colonised country that suffered for over three hundred years. Dealing with the shocking legacy of our clueless, colonialist ancestors has a long way to go, especially with the wilful ignorance promoted by the government here," says Stephanie in a staccato as passionate as a coloratura soprano singing Mozart's, Queen of the Night.

"Yes, Steph, I fully understand your passion and I agree. I suffered that guilt-by-association when I was living in Solo. We must do justice to the fabrics at least! I'll get started on a pattern tomorrow morning. I'll need some calico to make a toile."

"Would a worn-out sheet do instead, Lara? We try to recycle as much as possible?"

"An old sheet will be fine; Steph, and a broadsheet newspaper will do for the patterns. That's what Saraswati always used. Actually, I still have her kebaya patterns in Yogyakarta," I blurt out brightly, as if the patterns might come in handy one day, when in fact the sudden memory of them has made me dizzy. I know that Saraswati's patterns will never be used again. The joy she brought to them is forever buried; her measurements, scribbled in blue ink, have become a requiem:

payudara (bust) 75 cms
pinggang (waist) 65 cms
pinggul (hips) 80 cms

56

These 'pond' stays with Grace and Stephanie and those with Kathleen and Amy managed to keep the floundering fish of me afloat. Weeks turned into months as did the visits to Janice, the family lawyer.

My father must have held a conference with a few of his departed colleagues from the courts to find my family lawyer, Janice, then he must have channelled a request through Shirley, the solicitor I'd been to see about the house. I'd been losing a bit of trust in the universe, but after I met these two women, I started to get it back.

When I first met Shirley, my plan was simply to have her change the title on the house in case Angus decided to marry again, because even though he always said he wouldn't, I had a long list of other things he said he would never do, and had done, or was doing. I'd lost some trust in the universe and didn't have much trust left in Angus either. I was in a state of high anxiety.

If the house was left in joint names, and he remarried, and I died, Amar could lose any inheritance. Amar loved the house as much as I did. And of course, by the time I'd blurted all this out to the solicitor, I was crying. She said,

"Lara, look at me. He doesn't need to get married to put you in a vulnerable situation. You need to cut loose, girlfriend."

The lawyer looked and was starting to sound comfortingly like Maria. She had the same soft brown eyes, the same bob cut hair and a witty sense of humour, which was needed as much as the tissue box she slid towards me. She was a bit taller than Maria when she stood up, and tall in her swivel chair when she sat across the desk from the blubbering mess of me and chewed her pen as she listened.

"You need to speak with a family lawyer, Lara. I can recommend a woman who'll be just right for you. She's been through a divorce herself. How about I make an appointment for you now?"

"Okay," I blubbered, grabbing a tissue.

"Janice can see you tomorrow. Go home and watch a movie or something. Get some ice cream on the way. There's a Baskin Robbins on Waterworks Road. You need to zone out for a while."

"I know the Baskin Robbins shop," I sniffled, in a fresh stream of tears as I told her how Angus had once run home with a melting caramel toffee cone for me.

The background story I shared with Shirley was then shared with my family lawyer, Janice, along with a few other snippets, even though I was well aware that her time was my money, especially as Maria, who had frequent dealings with corporate lawyers in her secretarial job, kept reminding me.

The reason was Janice herself. She was such a kind woman. Shirley had been right. The two of us connected at the first meeting. If Shirley had sat tall in her swivel chair when I told her my story, Janice sat taller.

"You've been through a lot," she said, sliding a box of tissues towards me just as Shirley had done. "But what a life you've built for yourself there, Lara. Keep hold of that. It hasn't disappeared, it's just waiting for your return." Then she swivelled back in her chair and slowly stood up. She poured two glasses of water from a crystal jug, condensing its icy contents onto a stainless-steel tray and passing me one, said.

"Drink this, Lara, we've got work to do. We need to get you back to this nice man, Harto."

57

After a few months of this 'lawyer's office to ponds' routine, the tenants move out of the house in Brisbane. They've forgotten to sign a new lease. The cosmos has aligned in my favour. A decent deposit of good karma is back in my wallet. They move out, with their ten-year-mess-of-group-share-things, and my gracious old home in Brisbane is empty.

I buy a single mattress and move back in for the space. And that space becomes a healing sanctuary, as do the familiar smells of buckinghamia and orange blossom. The secluded pool in the back garden becomes my River Ganges—my River Nile. I start to reclaim the garden.

All summer long, the gardenia flowers bloom then rust and wilt, and the bougainvillea weaves its thorny vines through the trees, dressing their branches in fuchsia patterned prints. Star wisteria flowers propel themselves onto the pool, sprinkling purple petals on its glass surface until it becomes a temple bath. A selamatan. A celebration.

Though I'm lonely without Harto, in that space, on my single mattress, in that empty house, I'm free. Free to call him whenever I want. At night we talk for hours. The wrench from him eases into a new routine. The space has brought him back into my immediate world. We see each other on our small screens every night. After calling we send kisses and hearts. We decide since I've been gone for more than a year that it's better not to renew the lease on the house in Bausasran. With a neighbour he prepares a storeroom in the kampung. Over a few weeks they transfer all the furniture out on a tray truck in small loads, sparing me at least from a formal farewell to the house I loved. He jokes to ease my sadness, saying the termites are living like kings in my absence. They've chewed enough wood to weaken the eves. One has crashed to the ground.

One night he mentions in passing that he's recently attended a high-school reunion; and that his old school friends have arranged to catch up from time to time. I'm happy to hear that he isn't lonely, and I don't think more about it. I'm living alone in in my old family home, but on a small screen at night, I'm not. Harto and I are as together as ever, or so I think. We joke and we laugh and we cry. We always make each other feel better.

And I'm not alone during the days, because the birds visit. They come to drink from the pool and dip their feathers—shake them out on the black steel fence. The kookaburras laugh. The magpies and the butcherbirds warble, and the sulphur-crested cockatoos fly overhead like cartoon birds in a perfect cartoon sky and squawk, and sometimes fly down to perch on the canvas sail over the deck, cocking their heads, just as my friends and family do when they drop in to check that I'm okay. And the lizards come too, and small green frogs and water dragons. Palm trees rustle their fronds in the breezes, bringing the sounds of Bausasran with them. Butterflies, painted in yellows and cream come to busy themselves; and dragonflies hover their stained-glass helicopter wings above the water. How can I not smile? How can I not be happy with this loot? This gift!

I feel blessed, but I'm sad too, because all this will be lost. And I feel burdened with a weight as blunt as a rubber mallet—a judge's gavel. I'm in the middle of a divorce and property settlement, and this house, this healing space, will soon be sold. These sights; these sounds; and these smells that were once my home. There is no other choice.

Then one day, while I'm doing laps in the temple bath, a solution dawns on me and I climb out and snatch my sarong from the fence. Run inside in my flip-flops; almost trip over a loose paving stone in my rush. Dripping temple water with me as I run up the creaky back steps. I grab my phone from the kitchen bench. My hands still wet. And standing there in a puddle of pool water on the creaking timber floorboards, wrapped in a beach towel that Alin sent as a gift, I call Amar.

"Hi Amar, do you have a minute? I have an idea!"

"I'm at work Mum, but sure, what's up?"

"How about you buy my half of the house?"

"Hey, that's not a bad idea, Mum. Actually, I just got a bonus from the last building project."

"That's great news Amar. Maybe the stars are aligning in our favour."

"Not sure I believe in the stars but it was fun having a grandmother who did."

"Yes Amar, if she was still here, she could read our tea leaves."

"Grandma would agree anyway, Mum. She loved the old house. How about I call the big guy tonight? See what he thinks."

"Thanks, Amar, and by the way, I found a cottage up on the range near Grace and Stephanie's place. It's a bit rundown but it has a good feel."

"Sounds cool, Mum, but I have to go! I'll call you back later tonight."

"Sure, Amar. Call the big guy first," I reminded. "I'll keep my fingers crossed."

I hung up the phone with renewed hope. When Amar called back, he had good news. Angus had agreed with the idea.

"That's a huge relief Amar," I sighed, then I told him about the cottage. I warned him the boards of the verandah needed replacing, and the knotted pine walls inside needed painting, the old carpet would have to go and the kitchen needed updating. I confessed the corrugated iron roof was rusting in spots but there was a redeeming feature. The ceilings were high like the house in Brisbane, and the house in Bausasran. Amar laughed, saying it sounded like my style.

"Might take me a while but I can fix it all for you," he chuckled, then he talked about how much Alin and Kee were enjoying the move from Jakarta to Sydney, and how surprised Alin had been to see Australians wearing rubber flip-flops in the street. She'd bought a pair for the beach. He said he would fly up to Brisbane soon with Kee, to check the cottage. Alin would be away visiting her mother in Jakarta.

58

Two weeks later Amar flew up to Brisbane with Kee. He arrived at the airport with his Jesus Christ Superstar slash Dolce and Gabbana model looks and his smile. After all, I was looking through a pair of sunshine-tinted glasses. And then there was Kee, with her running-to-me smile that jumped up into my arms, spreading kisses all over me until I turned into a glow worm.

"Immmmmaaaa."

"Keeeeeeeeeee."

I hadn't ever pushed Kee with the correct pronunciation for 'grandma'. Better to leave some things just as they are—as naturally as the first time they flow out into the world.

She glued herself to my hip as I followed Amar, forgetting that he wasn't familiar with the recently-revamped domestic airport until he said,

"Mum, I should be following you."

"My sense of direction is poor Amar. I was trusting yours."

"Right, Mum. Do you remember which level you parked on?"

"Hold on, I took a photo, Amar," I say, fishing in my tote bag with my left hand, rendered weaker from all its polite years in Java. And still I refuse to put Kee down.

"Kee's big enough to walk Mum. You'll hurt your back."

"Okay Amar, but don't let go of my hand, Kee. And pinch my arm so I know you're really here."

"I missed you, Ima."

"I missed you too, Kee."

Amar and Kee had arrived on a Saturday morning with only a weekend to spare from work and school. We drove straight up to the range so Amar could confirm that the country cottage, though in need of repairs, was not about to fall down.

On the way back down the mountain we stopped in at Australia Zoo, as a treat for the animal lover in Kee. In all the years that Amar and I lived in Brisbane we had never been. As soon as we passed through the ticket counter, Kee caught sight of the snake handler and started running towards her.

"Keeeeee, slow down. Wait for us!" I called after her, but she was already engaged in animated conversation with a young woman dressed in khakis and desert boots and a snake, as a living boa, around her neck and shoulders.

"This snake is called a python. It isn't venomous," she told Kee, with a comforting authority. "But most snakes are, so you have to be very careful. Come on. Would you like to feel the skin?"

"Okay, answered Kee obligingly, but I want to feed the kangaroos more!"

"Good idea, Kee," I agreed, preferring animals with legs.

Amar chuckled with fatherly pride at all this, taking it in his sure stride as he held her right hand. I was more serious as I held her left and she began to skip along the path.

"Kee, you could be a zookeeper in the future. Add it to you list of dreams."

"Yes, Ima. I can be a zookeeper and a singer, and you forgot artist and film director!"

"You can be anything that makes you happy Kee. Let's sing the list!"

1. Entomologist, specialising in butterflies.
2. Builder like Papa.
3. Open a restaurant with Mama (because her cooking is the best and everyone should try it).
4. Scientist (mission: to invent a pill that makes grandmothers live forever).
5. Zookeeper (especially kangaroo or snake feeder).

And so, the day skipped along until we'd had enough fun and enough sun and we headed back to Brisbane with Amar at the wheel again.

That night we slept at the house in Brisbane on a makeshift bed on the floor made from two single mattresses pushed together. In a triple cuddle we listened to Kee read a bedtime story about a bear from a picture book Aunty Amy had brought back from Canada.

"Once upon a time there was a bear cub called Grizzly. She was lost and alone and beginning to get hungry…"

Kee had made a firm decision at age three that she would speak only one language. She chose English and spoke it with great flair and expression.

"I'm English", she would say determinedly, with Disney accent.

"Yes Kee! You and only you know exactly who you are!"

The only other language Kee spoke was when, with her button nose and her little palms held together and facing Mecca, she recited her bedtime prayer. The one that Alin had taught her to say from the time she could speak. The first line in Arabic:

> *Bismika Allahumma ahyaa wa bismika amuut*
> O Allah, with your name I live and die

Then, in an accent that emulated her mother's she would recite:

Ya Allah, berikanlah aku dan keluargaku,
Kesehatan dan umur panjang
Ya Allah, berikanlah pekerjaan yang bagus buat Papaku
Ya Allah, jauhkan aku dari orang jahat
Ya Allah, terima kasih atas
Rahmat dan Hidayah Mu
Amin

O Allah, please give me and my family
Health and long life,
O Allah, please provide good work for Papa,
O Allah, keep me far from bad people,
O Allah, thank you for your
Mercy and Guidance,
Amen.

Amar and Kee's visit was as fast as a magic carpet ride. And faster on the way to the airport with Amar in the driver's seat!

When we parted ways at the airport Kee's face alternated between smiles and frowns, because she hadn't seen her great-grandmother, Kathleen. Kee thought of her the way she thought of Mother Goose or the old woman who lived in a shoe.

"Give me some extra hugs, Kee. I will deliver them for you."

"Mum, enough hugs. We have to go! We'll see you again soon!"

"Yes, Amar! Love you. Love you Kee."

"Love you, Ima."

"Love you, Mum. Hang in there. Things will work out. And what about my hug!"

"Oh yes of course, Amar! I didn't forget. You're after Kee!"

On the way back from the airport I dropped into Kathleen's to deliver the hugs as promised. Over tea and shortbread, I mentioned how everything was suddenly falling in to place. Like the last few pieces of a jigsaw puzzle.

That's when she told me again, one of her stories I loved to hear. About how she'd moved house so many times the cups and saucers knew which box to jump into! She never began her stories with 'once upon a time', but it felt like she did.

As an army wife, Kathleen had moved house twenty-six times—from Tasmania in the south of Australia, to Townsville in the north, and she had once moved countries to Singapore. Sometimes the postings were short but most lasted for two years.

The one she preferred to talk about, and the one she remembered best, was the posting to Singapore. She would never forget the orchid corsage, and the silk shantung dress she bought to wear in the evenings, in lilac, a colour that suited her strawberry blond hair. The hair that rarely saw a salon in Australia was, for those two years, coiffured. She said that Singapore allowed her to be a lady—a lady of leisure.

She remembered the tang and fizz of the Singapore slings she sipped with the other Army wives at Raffles, and she remembered the waiters and the wicker chairs; the sheer decadence of a brandy and dry before lunch. She remembered the silverware and the fine China teacups they drank from, and the orange pekoe tea. These women had escaped from the drudgery of housework that tied their generation down. They revelled in their two-year passes to freedom. Released from the constant polishing of linoleum floors and the pressure of turning a light sponge cake out of the oven.

Kathleen was forever grateful to lovely old Ah Toh the amah, who, with her stoop and her lotus-bound-feet had cared so much for the children. And Rose. She remembered Rose, the younger housemaid—how slim and elegant she was, how funny and how kind. She said it wrenched her heart to remember the lonely figures of them at the airport, waving, when the family left. She always wondered how they'd fared later, especially Ah Toh, with her cobbled feet. She said she sometimes still missed them half a century later.

Ah Toh and Rose had unknowingly reprieved her from a life of ironing starched army uniforms. They had given her time to look in the mirror; time to powder her nose; time to slap on some lipstick and time to play with her friends. Those two years in Singapore sustained Kathleen through all the other years of her married life. The memories of them romanced with her. Danced cheek-to-cheek with her. Whenever I listen to Kathleen reel back to those nectar years of her youth, the signs of age that have claimed her skin retreat and return her complexion to summer peaches and cream.

"Kathleen, do you remember when we went to the tea plantation in Guilin with Amy, and we had the Chinese tea ceremony with the guide?"

"Yes Lara, I remember. The guide poured boiling water all over the tiny clay teapot before making the tea."

"That's right Kathleen. And she said that after the teapot has been used for a while it retained the tea's flavour; that you no longer needed to add the tea leaves. As though the pot remembered the taste of the tea. Just the way you remember those days in Singapore so well."

"Yes, Lara, that's very true. Do you remember browsing in the souvenir shop? Amy bought a canister of fragrant tea. The leaves unfolded like flowers. I think it was called Osmanthus."

"Ah yes, I remember Kathleen, and I've always remembered a proverb I learned from the guide. She said it only takes one flower to make a fragrance. And isn't it true."

"That's true of some places and some people, Lara."

"Yes, Kathleen, and just as Singapore is your fragrant flower, so Yogyakarta is mine. As soon as things are settled here, I'll go back to visit for a while. I so miss the smells."

59

The following day, I made an appointment to see Janice and another one to see Shirley. Janice shook her head at me settling for less and was only comforted by the hope that my sewing skills and my language teaching skills would make for a survival kit.

"If you ever decide to start a fashion label, make sure you design some stylish things for women with larger figures like Shirley and me," she reminded.

Shirley had to be convinced that the cottage was the right decision, and that I wasn't following my heart when I should be following my head. Because, she reminded me, my heart was what got me into trouble before. I had to reassure her that the cosmos had found the cottage for me but she shot a sceptical look over the tops of her glasses. Then, like Janice, she asked if I could bring back some batik fabrics from Jalan Solo, and wished me the best and said to give her best to Harto.

Within a few weeks all the court documents were signed and archived. I was finally free to travel. My only thought was to get back to Yogyakarta to see Harto.

Amy drove me up the mountain to collect the keys to the cottage. We glanced around at the avalanche of repairs that needed to be done and clicked the front door closed again. Then we drove straight back down the mountain to her place in Brisbane where my packed bags and my ticket to Yogyakarta were waiting along with a quiche she had made in advance from the Women's Weekly cookbook.

Grace and Stephanie drove down the mountain with their overnight bags, a bottle of French champagne and a large lemon meringue pie made from their bumper crop of lemons. They were loaded up with nuts and candies for me to take as oleh-oleh gifts for Harto and others they remembered from their trip to Yogyakarta.

On the way to Amy's they had collected Kathleen so the five of us could drink a toast without having to drive afterwards.

The celebrations kicked off with Aretha Franklin belting out 'Sisters doin' it for Themselves', from the large screen TV in the living room. We raised our glasses and sang the chorus, except for Kathleen who wasn't familiar with the lyrics but tapped her feet supportively. Then we switched to more mellow songs by Nina Simone while we enjoyed the quiche. Even though I knew Amy was tempted to play James Taylor she knew not to, because although Angus no longer held a resemblance to the young James Taylor on the cover of *Sweet Baby James* (and neither did the real James Taylor) the old associations were best avoided.

"Thank you for helping me through these last two years," I said, holding up my glass to toast the four vivacious and independent women sitting on the back deck at Amy's.

"You're our sister! We love you!" they shouted, clinking their glasses while Kathleen complimented Amy again on the delicious quiche Lorraine.

"Well, I love you all too, and you'll be happy to know you can sleep your hangovers off in the morning. Maria is driving me to the airport."

"Cheers to Maria!" they all replied, tipsily.

"Maria is very kind! Now, who'd like some lemon meringue pie?" asked Grace, off to the kitchen to fetch dessert plates.

--oOo--

Early next morning Maria drove me to Brisbane International airport.

"Lara, are you sure you don't have any Italian in your bloodline. Look at us, with our Roman noses," Maria pointed out, focusing the smart phone camera as we posed for a selfie in the parking bay. "We could be twins except that you're still too thin. Say hello to Harto for me and look after yourself, Lara. Have you got your passport? Ticket? Wallet?"

"Yes, Maria, but I'll check again while you're still here."

"Text me when you arrive in Yogyakarta Lara, so I know you're okay and give Harto my best and tell him to think about moving here. I hope it all goes well Lara. Keep in touch if it's not a hassle, otherwise just enjoy yourself and I'll see you soon."

"Thanks Maria, and thanks for being you."

"Don't go soft now, Lara. You need to keep a bit of that lioness," she winked, before donning her dark glasses. Then, with a last wave through the wound-down passenger window of her trusty black BMW, she disappeared into the stream of airport traffic. Maria's secretarial skills had taught her to file things in compartments. I knew she was pushing the concerns she felt for me further down her list. At least until she'd completed more pressing tasks.

Two years after the marathon of my divorce, I was finally back in the gate lounges of Brisbane International Airport waiting to fly back to Yogyakarta. My permanent residency visa had long since expired so I was a tourist again on a one-month visa without a firm plan. All I knew was I had to see Harto again. The wrench had been so sudden.

On video calls in the previous weeks, we had arranged to take a road trip to Semarang, in order to spend some time alone together.

"Let's stay at Candi Baru Hotel, Pang. It has the nostalgic feel of the house in Bausasran."

"Okay Lara, and still not too expensive. You must be more careful with your money now."

"Yes Pang, and I will need to teach again soon. But I want to see you first."

"I will be happy to see you too, Lara. Be careful on the way. Keep your eyes sharp. Don't be too friendly with everyone. And there's no need to bring oleh-oleh."

"I will text from the airport in Brisbane, Pang," and so I did.

60

There is no other place in the world like Indonesia. Even if you wore a blindfold you would know it by its smell. As if all the scents of it: jasmine flowers and ginger, ripe mangoes and rotting peels, tuber roses and incense sticks, have all been pulverized with clove cigarettes. Crushed together in a mortar like a mixture of rendang spice, then scooped up and made into a candle, lit and set adrift in a paper boat with a prayer, to infuse all its aromatic vapours into the warm trade winds, on its seventeen-thousand-island travels.

These were the scents that greeted me and filled my lungs with relief when I landed at Adisucipto International Airport in Yogyakarta after the long saga of my divorce with Angus was finally over. I hadn't seen Harto in the flesh for over two years.

And there he was, just as always. The moment I caught sight of his face in the crowd I felt all that time evaporate into the familiar sights and sounds and smells around me. The friendly calls in a language I had missed coming from the mouths of trolley hands and taxi drivers. I felt that at long last I was back home. Harto lifted my suitcase from the airport trolley, as he had always done before and we headed for the car. I fixed my eyes on him to make up for all the lost time. I commented on how healthy he looked. He smiled and said I looked beautiful. He said he'd finally learned to swim after all these years. He'd taken regular lessons at the public pool.

After a few hours of driving through familiar scenes of green and gold, we arrived at the hotel. As we climbed the stairs to our room, he mentioned he had a friend. Instantly, I felt the blood drain from my body, creating an invisible pool at my feet, rendering me to stone—as still as the statues that stand in Candi Sewu temple.

Summoning all my strength I whispered, "Will you marry her," knowing deep down the answer would be yes.

"Lara, you bought a house. I thought you would not come back."

"I bought a house for security, Pang. Not a home. It isn't a house like the warm one we shared in Taman Pinang, or the house you built from sand for Saraswati, or the tiny house in Purwanggan where your mother raised you, or as elegant as the house in Brisbane, and there will never be another house like the one in Bausasran that holds all our dreams, Pang. And you are not in it. My home will always be wherever you are." But it's already too late.

"She's an old classmate from school, Lara. Her husband of many years was a man who could not control his anger. Punched her black and blue. Her two grown sons have followed him. Become the same. I can offer her shelter. And soon you will see Mbah Salim, Saraswati's mother. You will see she is getting old now. Her hair is as white as this T-shirt I am wearing. She no longer paints it black. A Javanese wife can help with her care in the future and help me run the ronde stall when she eventually joins her daughter. How about you meet her when we go back to Yogyakarta?"

"Forgive me Pang, but I'm too tired after all I've been through, and like Saraswati's mother I'm getting older. I know you will treat this woman well, in the same way that you cared for me so gently."

"Lara we are both getting older. And I too am tired."

He kissed my tears away. He told me to always wear the gold wedding ring he placed on my finger all those years ago, when he told me the legend of Roro Jonggrang as we sat in the ruins of Candi Sewu.

"With this ring I am still strong beside you," he promised. "I will always be beside you." But as he said it, a tear escaped and rolled down his cheek and I watched the heart of this strong man, who had carried my pain through all the years since Angus left, breaking with me. And I looked at him for a long while and thought, but I didn't say: "You will always be my king of hearts, Pang. There will never be another."

"Can we go back to Yogyakarta tomorrow?" I asked blankly instead. "I want to visit to Mbah Salim at the ronde stall and drink ginger tea, and say goodbye to Bhima, since I may not see him for a while. And I want to go to the cemetery and say a prayer for Saraswati, and visit your mother's grave to pay my respects. We will need two baskets of flower petals. There are so many things to organise since I won't stay long. Your friend must be waiting for you and you will need to make your wedding plans. I suppose you have told her that I am Juragan and nothing more."

But Harto didn't answer any of this with words. Instead, in the ashram stillness of the room in the Candi Baru Hotel, where we lay watching the sky through cathedral windows from the bed, he began to trail a swathe of soft kisses from my face to my feet.

"Come, Lara, let's take a shower. I will wash your hair," he said, kissing my tears and I thought: He's here now. Here I am, held in his arms. But I will lose this. Lose the feel of his breath and his skin close to mine; never feel his hands gently stroke my face, never again run my fingers through the close crop of his hair. Never watch his graceful movements and feel the stillness he brings into a room. Never shower or bathe together again, or while away the hours of another warm afternoon in bed. And so, I whispered,

"Can we stay like this, just as we are now? I want this feeling of space to last for a while longer. We can watch the clouds scud their full curtains across the windows before night falls."

"Lara, just go to sleep here on my chest. I will hold you tight. In the morning we can shower and I will wash your hair."

By morning I thought I would survive. The last two years had made me stronger. I still had Amar and Alin and little Kee, and who knows how many more like her. And I had my family of sisters and all my friends. Maybe I could visit Franciskus at the seminary in Flores. Teach English to the students there. He always said he would take me to Komodo Island to see the dragons. Or maybe I could sail around the Banda Islands like Sheena.

Ibu, bule, sendiri, mandiri.
Woman, white, single, independent.

As Harto lathered me in the shower, I told him that I would stay a few weeks at Puri Artha hotel. That I could relax there. Visit Harold and Carl and Nurani and Maulina, and that I had so many teachers to visit from two schools. I asked if he could take me to Mirota handicraft store as usual to shop for dresses and kerudung scarves. I told him I could walk to the fabric shops in Jalan Solo from there, but asked if he would drive me to Gramedia, because I wanted to browse the bookshelves and probably buy some more books. Books are heavy to carry, I reminded him. He said he would come during the days to drive me wherever I wanted to go as always and then he kissed my cheeks, and my forehead and combed my hair in the rust speckled wardrobe mirror.

"Let's go to Parangtritis on our way back to Yogyakarta, Pang. We can sit on the cliffs together and watch the waves and the coastal birds one last time."

"Promise you will come back to visit, Lara. Promise it won't be the last time."

"Let's see what the future brings Pang. The country cottage I bought needs a lot of fixing so it doesn't fall down like the house in Bausasran. Maybe when that's done, I can rent it out. Come back to visit. Who knows? Maybe I'll build a bamboo house in Bantul and grow old there. You can visit me. Drive me wherever I need to go.

When you helped me rebuild my life Pang, you helped me build my strength."

I don't tell him that my strength is more like fired clay, not steel or metal. That it can easily shatter. I will not bring myself to ruin his chance at happiness.

--oOo—

Neither Harto nor I ever really entertained the idea of marriage, even after Saraswati passed away. In Java, marriage is a family affair. The idea was as remote as the distant moon, never entering the world we occupied together. We were each other's temporary shelter, though we often talked of growing old together.

"Even when you are eighty years old and walk with a stick, I will still love you, Lara."

"And I will love you, Pang, until my dying day."

Words of certainty thrown into the 'never-knowing' of what life might bring. Harto gave me the gift of time—the patience I needed to recover and grow, to learn and to survive what I thought I couldn't. For a while, we walked together and he taught me to walk the path of life—to let the future unfold as it will, like the petals of a lotus flower.

I've always preferred dawn over dusk. That dreamtime space between asleep and awake. And if memory like the dawn is a dream state, then in the mists of mine is a life I lived in Java. The memories of it caught forever in the hands of time.

But for now, it's time to rest my pen and dream once again. To dream of star jasmine vines and plantation shutters painted green, of palm trees rustling in the breeze, of marble table tops and rattan chairs and wicker trays of tea, and to salute the past and the years we spent together in the house in Bausasran.

After storms have settled and moved out to sea in their own time we begin to trust again in the shifting winds. Now I know to trust as much in storms. Storms can bring the best of friends.

Acknowledgements

There are many people who encouraged me to write this story, but especially Kerry Kilner, who believed in me more than I believed in myself. Your enthusiasm, professional advice and insightful editing have been a lifebuoy. Angela Gardner for teaching me a writer's discipline and other tips. You were right, six pages is not a book! Thanks to you I kept going. Anton, for your support every step of the way and for the generous supply of coffee from Flores. Circle Brophy for your constant support and friendship, and for the illustrations which I love. Susan Agustina for sharing your wealth of linguistic knowledge so graciously. Cheryl Reid for coming to Yogyakarta and snapping the gorgeous cover photo. Carly Gordyn for reminding me to 'get the ring to Mordor'. Aka, for your endless help, proofreading patience, and for being a stern big sister when needed. My 'sista' Anne, for your many 'final' draft readings, formatting skills and wise suggestions—and for the spare bed.

To Cath, for keeping my spirits up with just the right words. Siobhan, for that look of surprise when you read the first few pages in Yogya years ago. I hope the rest does not disappoint! Tara for the '*ting ting ting*'...you're a glassful of inspiration! Petrina, your banana muffins and company helped, and so did the salads. Ibu Ulida, my Indonesian 'twin'. Reading your story inspired me to finish writing mine. Mbak Swiny, for all the Pilates sessions and critiques of early drafts in Yogyakarta cafes, and for always finding the best *rujak* ice cream. Mbak Mike Mariana, my Indonesian language teacher, fellow bookworm and roasted corn lover. Mbak Novita for your kindness and support.

My heartfelt thanks always to the residents of kampung Surokarsan, whose generosity and stories have been the greatest gift. And last but not least thank you to my son, RJ, for always being proud of me no matter what—and for the necessary bear hugs.

Author's Note

The House in Bausasran is a blend of fact and fiction based on two periods of my life spent in Java. Where characters are, or have been public figures associated with the meditation group Sumarah, I have used real names. The names of famous figures used for cultural or contextual reference have been kept. Otherwise, I have invented certain characters or used pseudonyms in order to respect the lives of those involved in mine. All locations and place names are actual.

Solo, Central Java 1981

Tree of Life on silk, Yogyakarta 2004

Baron Beach 2008

Glossary

arisan: lottery club
ayam: chicken
baju: clothing/outfit
banyak: a lot/many
becak: pedicab
blangkon: traditional Javanese batik headdress for men
boleh: may/can
buang: throw away
bubur: porridge
besar: big
dalang: puppeteer
dulu: before
emas: gold
gelap: dark
gayung: water dipper
gembira: cheerful
hati-hati: be careful
janji: promise
juragan: employer/boss
kain: fabric/cloth
kasihan: such a pity
kebaya: traditional blouse
kecil: small
kerudung: head scarf/veil
klepon: pandan coloured sticky-rice sweets
kribo: frizzy hair
oleh-oleh: small gifts (often food)
muda: young

nanti: later
negara: country
oseng-oseng: stir fry
paranormal: psychic
pasar: market
peci: prayer hat
pelit: stingy
perak: silver
pembantu: domestic helper
pendopo: gazebo-style building
pesan: message
rompi: vest
sama-sama: you're welcome
sanggul: bun (hairstyle)
sarung: sarong
serabi: rice flour pancake
silahkan: please
silahkan coba: please try
simbah: grandparent *(Javanese)*
sindur: a red wedding shawl
susu: milk/breast
tahu: tofu
tanggal: date
tenggelam: drown
tikus: rodent
titip: entrust belongings with someone
tua: old
tukang: craftsman, workman, handyman
warung: food stall